ENGLISCH 7/8

Wir üben

Grammatik – Übersetzung – Wortschatz

von Wolfgang Kurschatke,
Hannes Gumtau und Ian Traynor

MANZ VERLAG MÜNCHEN

Herausgegeben von Ute Kretschmann

Mitarbeiter:
Ian Traynor, M.A., M.A. (Aberdeen)
Gisela Gumtau, Schongau (Zeichnungen)

Manzbuch 504

8 7 6 5   1993 92 91 90 89
(Die jeweils letzte Zahl bezeichnet die Auflage bzw. das Erscheinungsjahr)

Umschlagentwurf: Ingeburg Rothemund, München
Gesamtherstellung: Verlag und Druckerei G. J. Manz AG, München/Dillingen
Printed in Germany

ISBN 3-7863-0504-8

Inhalt

Lösungsheft

Kapitel 1

Arbeitsanleitungen
Sinnvolles Üben und Wiederholen

Liebe Schülerinnen und Schüler!

ENGLISCH 7/8
Wir üben **GRAMMATIK – ÜBERSETZUNG – WORTSCHATZ**

ist eine Lernhilfe für das 3. und 4. Lernjahr.

Sie schließt an die Lernhilfen **ENGLISCH 5/6** und **ENGLISCH 6/7** an und wird in **ENGLISCH 8/9** fortgesetzt.

In diesem Band könnt ihr die wichtigen Lerninhalte des 3. und 4. Lernjahres üben und wesentliche Abschnitte des Grundwissens wiederholen.
Für die **Vorbereitung** auf Stegreifaufgaben und Schulaufgaben sollt ihr die jeweiligen Kapitel im Inhaltsverzeichnis nachschauen und dann selbständig die Lernhilfen studieren und die Übungen und Tests bearbeiten.
Das **Lösungsheft** dient euch zur Kontrolle und Verbesserung eurer eigenen Vorschläge.

Dieser Band bietet euch die schwierigen Probleme im Englischen in typischen Aufgabenstellungen, wie sie in Prüfungen vorkommen. Natürlich braucht ihr das Buch nicht von A–Z 'durchzupauken', sondern sucht euch die gefragten Kapitel selbst aus.

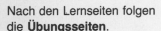

Am Anfang eines jeden Kapitels stehen
die **Lernhilfen** (L).
Hier werden Musterbeispiele und die entsprechenden Merkregeln dazu aufgeführt.

Nach den Lernseiten folgen
die **Übungsseiten**.
Die systematischen, lernzielorientierten Übungen werden den vielseitigen Anforderungen verschiedener Lehrpläne gerecht.
Die **Übersetzungen** in diesem Teil, sowohl Englisch–Deutsch, als auch Deutsch–Englisch, sollen ganz konkret das Verständnis eines Kapitels und deine Leistung überprüfen.

Die abschließenden **'Comprehension Tests'** (Textaufgaben) sind wirklich als Test zu verstehen. Ihr könnt hier zeigen, ob ihr ein Kapitel beherrscht.
Die Tests eignen sich natürlich auch als Hausaufgabe und zur zusätzlichen Übung in der Schule.

Unter all die Übungen und Tests hat
sich der **Fehlerteufel** gemischt, dessen
Unwesen ihr ein Ende bereiten sollt,
indem ihr die Fehler findet und verbessert.

Die **Wörterlisten** (W) bieten wichtige Vokabeln zu einzelnen Grammatikabschnitten. Die einfache deutsche Grundübersetzung erspart euch zeitraubendes Nachschlagen im Wörterbuch.

5

Wie kann ich mir Vokabeln besser merken?

Wir wollen dir das Lernprinzip aus ENGLISCH – 6. Jahrgangsstufe noch einmal näherbringen:

Vokabeln einschreiben – lernen – wiederholen

Du mußt jetzt unbedingt deine eigene Lernmethode gefunden haben. Entweder arbeitest du systematisch mit dem **Vokabelheft** oder der **Lernkartei**. Wir empfehlen dir weiterhin die Kartei.

Einschreiben

Alle neuen oder vergessenen Wörter schreibst du auf ein Kärtchen.
z. B.

century

a ~ is one
hundred years

Jahrhundert

Woher bekommst du die Bedeutung oder Erklärung?

Die neuen Wörter erscheinen meist in deinem Lehrbuch. Dort sind sie auch im Zusammenhang erklärt. Oft gibt auch der Lehrer eine Umschreibung der Wörter an. Die kannst du sofort in der Schule auf ein Kärtchen schreiben.

Lernen

Deine Kärtchen sammelst du in einem Karteikasten.

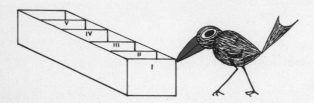

Neue Kärtchen nach I.
Lernen für die nächste Stunde   →   gelernte Kärtchen nach II.

Wiederholen

Möglichst regelmäßig, mindestens einmal pro Woche wiederholen:

Kärtchen aus II abfragen   →   gekonnte nach III
vergessene nach I

Kärtchen aus III abfragen   →   gekonnte nach IV
vergessene nach II
usw.

Wichtige Ratschläge:

1. Laß nie zu große Packen in den Fächern entstehen.
2. Setze feste Wiederholungszeit (z. B. samstags) fest.
3. Schreibe das englische Wort beim Lernen immer auf.
4. Wenn du ganz konsequent und ehrlich vorgehst, kannst du die Kärtchen im Fach V getrost herausnehmen und ablegen.

Kapitel 2

Der Gebrauch der Zeiten (The Tenses)

1.
Lernhilfen für die Übungen.
Simple Present oder Present Progressive (Continuous)?

Mr Brown **smokes**. He **smokes** every day. He **gets up** at six o'clock. It often **rains** in England.	**Simple Present** (Einfache Gegenwart): Etwas geschieht **regelmäßig, gewohnheitsmäßig, immer, oft!** <u>Signalwörter</u>: usually, always, often, on Mondays, at six, never, on Saturdays.
What **are** you **doing**, Ian? I **am going** to school. Look! Mr Brown **is** just **coming**.	**Present Progressive** (Verlaufsform der Gegenwart): Etwas "verläuft" **gegenwärtig!** <u>Signalwörter</u>: Look! Listen! now, at the moment, just.
Listen! I **hear** a noise. I am hungry, I **want** to eat. The house **belongs** to Mr Brown. I **understand** what you are saying.	**Simple Present** bei einigen Verben (Sinneswahrnehmung, Wollen, Zustand)! → Paukliste **5**

Häufige Fehler:
a) Kein -s in der 3. Person Singular (richtig: Tom eat**s**; she come**s**)
b) Falsche Schreibweise der Endung (richtig: He hurr**ies**, he's stop**ping**)
c) Falsche Wortstellung (richtig: He **always** gets up early.)

2.
Do you see the difference?

a) It often .... (rain) in England, but it .... (not rain) today.

b) Mr Brown usually .... (travel) to work by train, but today he

.... (go) by car.

c) Water .... (boil) at 100° C. The water .... (boil) now. Shall I make the tea?

d) Mrs Brown .... (read) a lot of books, but she ....

(not, read) at the moment. She .... (play) tennis.

3.
Complete:

a) Mr Brown can't answer the phone because he .... (have) a bath.

b) He always .... (go) to Scotland for his holidays.

c) Mrs Brown can't come now. She .... (wash) her hair.

d) The boys can't play football now as it .... (rain)

e) A lot of tourists .... (visit) London every year.

f) Most of them .... (speak) a little English.

g) When you .... (travel) to London, don't forget to see the Tower.

h) What .... (you, do) at the moment? I .... (do) an English exercise.

4.

Translate into English:

a) Hört! Jean spielt gerade Gitarre. Sie spielt sehr gut.

....

b) Es tut mir leid, ich kann nicht kommen. Ich schreibe gerade einen Brief.

....

c) Was macht Peter gerade? Ich glaube, er macht seine Aufgaben.

....

d) Was machen Peters Eltern an den Abenden? Sie hören Musik oder sie lesen.

....

e) Wo ist Billy? Er hilft in der Küche.

....

f) Billy hilft jeden Nachmittag in der Küche.

....

g) Schau! Der Bus kommt. Er kommt alle 30 Minuten.

....

h) Tom hört gerade Radio. Er hört die Stimme des Sprechers.

....

i) Dieser Kuchen schmeckt nach Käse.

....

k) London liegt an der Themse.

....

l) Kannst du Jean sehen? Sie liegt auf dem Sofa.

....

5.
Paukliste: Verben, die üblicherweise nicht in der Verlaufsform verwendet werden.
Example: I **hear** a noise.

to feel	sich fühlen, spüren
to hear	hören
to look	aussehen
to see	sehen
to smell	riechen nach
to taste	schmecken nach
to believe	glauben
to doubt	bezweifeln
to imagine	sich vorstellen
to know	wissen, kennen
to mean	meinen, bedeuten
to remember	sich erinnern an
to think	denken, halten von
to understand	verstehen
to like	mögen, gern haben
to hate	hassen, nicht mögen
to need	brauchen
to prefer	lieber haben
to want	wollen
to belong to	gehören (zu)

Beachte!

It tastes of onion.	Es schmeckt nach Zwiebel.
Tom is tasting the fish.	Tom probiert den Fisch.
Tom feels happy.	Tom fühlt sich glücklich.
His mother is feeling his throat.	Seine Mutter tastet den Hals ab.
Tom looks tired.	Tom sieht müde aus.
He is looking at a girl.	Er schaut sich ein Mädchen an.
Tom sees a bird.	Tom sieht einen Vogel.
He's seeing his friend tonight.	Er besucht heute abend seinen Freund.
What do you think of it?	Was hältst du davon?
What are you thinking about?	Worüber denkst du gerade nach?

6.
Lernhilfen für die Übungen.
Past Tense oder Present Perfect?

Mr Brown **went** to Dublin <u>in 1981</u>. Tom **visited** Paris <u>two years ago</u>.	**Past Tense:** Etwas ist in der **Vergangenheit abgeschlossen!** <u>Signale</u>: In 1981, two years ago, last week, last year, when?
The boys **have gone** to school. Mother is alone.	**Present Perfect:** Etwas ist geschehen und wir interessieren uns für die Folgen! (Die Buben sind fort.)
My friend **has lived** in London since 1980. He is still there. He **has been writing** letters all day. He is still writing them.	Etwas, das in der Vergangenheit begonnen hat (1980!), dauert noch an (Er wohnt heute noch dort.)! Oft **Present Perfect Progressive!**
<u>How long</u> **have** you **known** Jean? <u>This is the first</u> dress that Mr. Brown **has liked**.	Etwas wird auf die Gegenwart bezogen! <u>Signale</u>: How long? It's the first/second . . .; up to now; always; often; since; for

Häufige Fehler:

a) Wörtliche Übersetzung (Ich habe gestern Tom gesehen.)
b) Falsche 3. Form (Past Participle) vor allem bei unregelmäßigen Verben
→ Paukliste **21**
d) Verwechslung von **since** (Monday, 8 o'clock) und **for** (a week)
d) Nichterkennen des Present Perfect (Ich lerne schon seit . . .
I've been learning . . .)

7.
Answer the questions:

a) When did you write the letter? I .... it last week.

b) When did you meet Susy? I .... her last Monday.

c) When did you see Mr Brown? I .... him two days ago.

d) When did you lose your purse? I .... it last month.

e) When did you go to the pub? I .... there last night.

f) When did he sell his car? He .... it two weeks ago.

g) When did he drink the whisky? He .... it last Sunday.

h) When did Peter come home? He .... home at ten last night.

8.
Answer the questions:

a) Did he go to England or <u>Wales</u>? He .... to Wales.

b) Did he choose English or <u>French</u>? He ....

c) Did he begin early or <u>late</u>? He ....

d) Did he throw a stone or a <u>chair</u>? He ....

e) Did he eat an apple or a <u>pear</u>? He ....

f) Did he drive to Dover or <u>Oxford</u>? He ....

g) Did he take a taxi or a <u>bus</u>? He ....

9.

They have just done it:

Example: Mrs Brown is buying a new dress.
         Mrs Brown has just bought a new dress.

a) Mr Brown is writing a letter.

....

b) Peter is doing an exercise.

....

c) Billy is asking a question.

....

d) Tom is opening his English book.

....

e) The girls are translating a letter.

....

f) Mrs Brown is having tea.

....

g) Ian is speaking to his girlfriend.

....

h) Ian and Tom are doing their homework.

....

i) Barbara is going home.

....

k) Mrs Brown is doing her shopping.

....

10.

Put into the Present Perfect Progressive:

Example: I've been learning English for three years.
Now I am perfect.

a) Mrs Brown .... (cook) all afternoon, but dinner is not ready yet.

b) Billy .... (spend) money all day, and he's broke.

c) Billy .... (watch) too much TV. His eyes are red.

d) Jimmy Slow .... (learn) English for five years, but he can't even read a newspaper yet.

e) She ought to stop work. She has a headache because she ....

.... (work) too long.

f) Have you seen my English book anywhere? I .... (look) for it for days.

g) The boys are tired because they .... (do) homework since two o'clock.

h) The dog .... (play) with my trousers; they are torn.

i) Mr Brown .... (drive) all day, and he's tired.

k) I .... (look) at this photo for ten minutes, but I can't see my sister in it.

l) Since I have been in London, I .... (try) to speak English.

11.

Mark the correct form:

a) I haven't seen you ☐ for Monday.
    ☐ since

b) I haven't seen you ☐ for a month.
    ☐ since

c) We've been here ☐ for three and a half years.
    ☐ since

d) They have lived in that town ☐ for 1975.
    ☐ since

e) We haven't read any books ☐ for Christmas.
    ☐ since

f) I haven't eaten any tomatoes ☐ for I was a boy.
    ☐ since

g) I haven't spoken English ☐ for four weeks.
    ☐ since

h) I haven't played with toys ☐ for my childhood.
    ☐ since

i) I haven't worn that dress ☐ for six years.
    ☐ since

k) Billy has worked here ☐ for eight years.
    ☐ since

l) It hasn't rained ☐ for three months.
    ☐ since

m) I haven't ridden a bicycle ☐ for at least a month.
    ☐ since

n) Miss Clever has been teaching at our school ☐ for one year.
    ☐ since

o) It has not been snowing ☐ for yesterday morning.
    ☐ since

p) We have been studying English ☐ for 1979.
    ☐ since

r) Tom has been waiting ☐ for half an hour.
    ☐ since

s) Tom has been waiting ☐ for half past eight.
    ☐ since

12.

Translate into English:

Example: Ich bin seit zehn Uhr hier.
           I have been here since ten o'clock.

a) Ich bin (schon) seit einer Stunde hier.

....

b) Ich warte (schon) zwei Stunden.

....

c) Ich lerne seit 1978 Englisch.

....

d) Herr Brown wohnt (schon) seit fünf Jahren hier.

....

e) Ich habe meine Schwester seit Ostern nicht mehr gesehen.

....

f) Bill arbeitet schon seit drei Jahren hier.

....

g) Es regnet schon seit letzten Montag.

....

h) Die Kirche steht hier schon seit dreihundert Jahren.

....

i) Seit wann lernst du schon Englisch?

....

k) Wie lange wartest du schon hier?

....

l) Wie lange kennst du Herrn Brown schon?

....

13.
Past Tense or Present Perfect?

a) When .... (Mr Brown, come)? – He .... (come) half an hour ago.

b) When Mr Brown .... (be) a boy, he .... (live) in a small village.

c) .... (you, see) Mr Green yesterday? – No, I ....

d) .... (you, see) Mrs Green this morning? Yes, I ....

e) Mr Brown .... (go) to Paris in 1980. He .... (never, be) to Germany.

f) I .... (lose) my watch; I don't know what time it is.

g) Billy .... (lose) his watch last week.

h) .... (you, read) Oliver Twist? – I .... (read) it two years ago.

i) Tom .... (pass) the test; he is so happy.

k) Peter .... (just, fall) from the apple tree. Last summer he

.... (fall) from the pear tree.

l) I'm sorry I can't come; my car .... (break down).

m) I'm sorry Mr Brown .... (leave) the office.

o) It's the first time I .... (do) this exercise.

18

14.
Translate into English:

a) Herr Brown lebt schon seit vielen Jahren in London.

....

b) Sein Freund hat ihn letzten Sommer besucht und sie hatten eine schöne Zeit in London.

....

c) Herr Brown war noch nicht in Deutschland, aber nächstes Jahr möchte er München besuchen.

....

d) Als Herr Brown seinen Freund am Flugplatz abholte, regnete es.

....

e) Nachdem der Regen aufgehört hatte, unternahmen sie einen kurzen Spaziergang.

....

f) Frau Brown spielte gerade Klavier, als sie zurückkamen.

....

g) Ihre Tochter Clara spielt schon seit vier Jahren Violine.

....

h) Sie spielen oft zusammen.

....

i) An diesem Abend haben sie für ihren Freund gespielt.

....

k) Dem Freund hat es in London gut gefallen.

....

15.

Hier hat der Fehlerteufel zugeschlagen!
Verbessere bitte alle Fehler aus Schülerarbeiten:

a) Ich habe gestern einen Brief geschrieben.
   I have written a letter yesterday.

   ....

b) Ich bin letzte Woche nach London gefahren.
   I have gone to London last week.

   ....

c) Wo ist John gewesen?
   Where is John been?

   ....

d) Seit wann wartest du auf mich?
   Since when do you wait for me?

   ....

e) Ich warte jetzt schon seit 20 Minuten.
   I wait for twenty minutes now.

   ....

f) Ich habe Frau Brown seit drei Monaten nicht mehr gesehen.
   I haven't seen Mrs Brown since three months.

   ....

g) Bist du nach Dublin oder nach Belfast gereist?
   Did you travelled to Dublin or to Belfast?

   ....

16.

Vorüberlegung: Simple Past oder Past Progressive?

Mr Brown **went** to Dublin in 1981. Tom **visited** Paris two years ago.	**Simple Past** (Einfache Vergangenheit): Etwas ist in der **Vergangenheit abgeschlossen!**
The night **was becoming** colder. What **were you doing** at ten? – **I was sleeping.** Mr Brown **was watching** TV, when the telephone rang. ↑ Simple Past!	**Past Progressive** (Verlaufsform der Vergangenheit): Etwas **verlief allmählich!** Eine Handlung **verlief zu einer bestimmten Zeit gerade!** Eine **gerade verlaufende** Handlung wurde durch eine andere unterbrochen!
Mr Brown **was reading** while his wife **was cooking**.	Zwei oder mehr Handlungen **verliefen gleichzeitig!**

17.
Complete:

a) Mrs Brown .... (cook) dinner when her husband arrived home.

b) Mr Brown asked: "What .... (you, do) at 7.30 yesterday?"

"I .... (shop) in the supermarket," she answered.

c) What .... (you, do) at school on 1st April at 9 o'clock? – I think

I .... (do) a test.

d) When Tom left the house, the sun .... (shine).

e) Billy .... (do) his homework, when the bell rang.

18.
Translate into English:

a) Was hast du gestern zwischen 8 und 9 Uhr gemacht?
   – Ich habe mein Fahrrad repariert.

   ....

   ....

b) Was habt ihr letzten Sonntag gemacht, als Peter heimkam?
   – Wir haben Karten gespielt.

   ....

   ....

c) Herr Brown wusch sein Auto, als es zu regnen anfing.

   ....

d) Herr Green wusch sein Auto letzten Sonntag.

   ....

19.
Vorüberlegung: Past Tense + Past Perfect

The thief **had run away**, when the police **came**.

Past Perfect
Dies geschah zuerst!
(The thief ran away.)

Past
Dies geschah später!
(Two minutes later the police came.)

Tom **had been** in bed for two hours, when he **heard** a noise.

Past Perfect
(He went to bed at ten.)

Past
(At twelve he heard a noise.)

20.

Complete:

a) After Billy .... (leave), Mr Brown **went** to bed.

b) Billy .... (be) sorry for the mistake he .... (make).

c) Billy .... (meet) a friend he .... (not see) for a long time.

d) Susy .... (give) Billy her address after she .... (leave).

e) After Mr Brown .... (read) the book, he .... (take) it back to the library.

f) After the guests .... (go), Mrs Brown .... (do) the washing-up.

g) As soon as Mr Brown .... (take) the medicine, he .... (feel) much better.

h) Billy .... (do) his homework, before his mother ....

.... (come) home.

i) Billy .... (tell) his teacher that his father .... (help) him.

k) Mrs Brown .... (not see) her friends for a long time, when she

.... (meet) them at a party last night.

l) Ian .... (go) to Dover, after he .... (spend) two months in Manchester.

21.
Paukliste wichtiger unregelmäßiger Verben:

Infinitive (Grundform)	Past Tense (1. Vergang.)	Past Participle* (Partizip Perfekt)	Deutsch
to be	was / were	been	sein
to bear	bore	borne	tragen
to beat	beat	beaten	schlagen
to become	became	become	werden
to begin	began	begun	beginnen
to bind	bound	bound	binden
to bite	bit	bitten	beißen
to blow	blew	blown	blasen
to break	broke	broken	brechen
to bring	brought	brought	bringen
to build	built	built	bauen
to burst	burst	burst	bersten
to buy	bought	bought	kaufen
to catch	caught	caught	fangen
to choose	chose	chosen	wählen
to come	came	come	kommen
to cost	cost	cost	kosten
to creep	crept	crept	kriechen
to cut	cut	cut	schneiden
to deal	dealt	dealt	(be)handeln
to do	did	done	tun
to draw	drew	drawn	ziehen, zeichnen
to drink	drank	drunk	trinken
to drive	drove	driven	treiben, fahren
to eat	ate	eaten	essen
to fall	fell	fallen	fallen
to feel	felt	felt	fühlen
to fight	fought	fought	kämpfen
to find	found	found	finden
to forget	forgot	forgotten	vergessen
to fly	flew	flown	fliegen
to get	got	got	bekommen
to give	gave	given	geben

to go	went	gone	gehen
to grow	grew	grown	wachsen
to hang	hung	hung	hängen
to have	had	had	haben
to hear	heard	heard	hören
to hide	hid	hidden	verstecken
to hit	hit	hit	schlagen
to hold	held	held	halten
to hurt	hurt	hurt	verletzen
to keep	kept	kept	halten
to know	knew	known	wissen, kennen
to lay	laid	laid	legen
to lead	led	led	führen
to leave	left	left	verlassen
to lend	lent	lent	leihen
to let	let	let	lassen
to lie	lay	lain	liegen
to lose	lost	lost	verlieren
to make	made	made	machen
to mean	meant	meant	meinen
to meet	met	met	treffen
to pay	paid	paid	zahlen
to put	put	put	stellen, legen
to read	read	read	lesen
to ride	rode	ridden	reiten, fahren
to ring	rang	rung	läuten
to rise	rose	risen	sich erheben
to run	ran	run	rennen, laufen
to say	said	said	sagen
to see	saw	seen	sehen
to sell	sold	sold	verkaufen
to send	sent	sent	senden, schicken
to set	set	set	setzen
to shake	shook	shaken	schütteln
to shine	shone	shone	scheinen
to show	showed	shown	zeigen
to shut	shut	shut	schließen
to sing	sang	sung	singen
to sit	sat	sat	sitzen

to sleep	slept	slept	schlafen
to speak	spoke	spoken	sprechen
to spell	spelt	spelt	buchstabieren
to spend	spent	spent	ausgeben, verbringen
to spread	spread	spread	verbreiten
to stand	stood	stood	stehen
to steal	stole	stolen	stehlen
to strike	struck	struck	schlagen
to swear	swore	sworn	schwören, fluchen
to sweep	swept	swept	fegen
to swim	swam	swum	schwimmen
to take	took	taken	nehmen
to teach	taught	taught	lehren
to tear	tore	torn	zerreißen
to tell	told	told	erzählen
to think	thought	thought	denken
to throw	threw	thrown	werfen
to understand	understood	understood	verstehen
to wake	woke/waked	waked/woken	aufwecken, -wachen
to wear	wore	worn	tragen
to weep	wept	wept	weinen
to win	won	won	gewinnen
to write	wrote	written	schreiben

* Past Participle (Partizip Perfekt; Mittelwort der Vergangenheit):
  Diese **3. Form** der Verben brauchst du für viele Zeiten!
  - I have **seen**
  - I had **seen**
  - I will have **seen**
  - I would have **seen**
  - He was **seen** und die anderen Formen des **Passivs!**

22.
Vorüberlegung: Wie drücke ich die Zukunft aus?

– **I'm going to do** all exercises in this book.	**going to + Infinitive:** Eine **feste Absicht** bzw.
– **It's going to snow.** I heard the weather forecast.	deutliche **Anzeichen** für etwas Zukünftiges liegen vor!

– Mr Brown **will be** forty next week.	**will-Future:** Das künftige Geschehen hängt **nicht**
– Where **will we be** next summer? – I don't know.	**vom persönlichen Willen** ab!
– If it rains **we'll stay** at home.	Im Konditionalsatz!
– I hope **we'll meet** again.	Nach Verben wie **I hope, I think, I expect, I suppose, I'm sure!**

Tom **is playing** tennis tonight. **We're coming** to see you tomorrow.	**Present Progressive:** Ein fester Plan mit genauer Angabe der nahen Zukunft liegt vor (next week; Monday)!

I'll be working all day tomorrow.	**Future Progressive:** Eine Handlung wird in Zukunft verlaufen!
Will you be travelling to Paris or to Rome?	Höfliche Frage! vgl. Will you travel? = Willst du reisen?

23.

Make sentences like the first sentence:

Example: Peter / do / exercise / tomorrow
Peter is going to do the exercise tomorrow.

a) Mr Brown / paint / house / next week

....

b) Mrs Brown / buy / dress / this afternoon

....

c) They / travel / Ireland / next month

....

d) They / sell / car / as soon as possible

....

e) They / repair / lamp / next winter

....

Example: sure / Mr Brown / enjoy / party
I am sure Mr Brown will enjoy the party.

f) hope / brother / visit / me / soon

....

g) expect / Billy / come / next Monday

....

h) suppose / my teacher / do / test / tomorrow

....

i) think / Mrs Brown / buy / new dress / when she has enough money

....

24.
Put into the immediate future of the Present Progressive:
Example: Peter is playing tennis with me this evening.

a) Bill .... (come) to see me tomorrow.

b) Mrs Brown .... (take) us to the zoo this afternoon.

c) She .... (leave) at seven.

d) .... (you, stay) at home tonight?

e) .... (you, go) to London on Sunday?

f) They .... (play) Beethoven at the concert tonight.

25.
Put into the future progressive form:
Example: She is sleeping / all afternoon
            She will be sleeping all afternoon.

a) He is flying / all day

....

b) We're writing to you / soon

....

c) She is talking / for at least another two hours

....

d) She's washing her hair / this evening

....

e) He's studying English / for two more years

....

f) What are you doing / in five years' time?

....

30

26.

Make these questions more polite:

Example: Will you be travelling to Paris or to Rome?

a) What are you going to do in Paris?

....

b) When are you going to leave?

....

c) When are you going to return?

....

d) Which film are you going to see?

....

e) When are you going to do your homework?

....

f) Are you going to Manchester again this week?

....

g) Are you going to play tennis with Tom on Sunday?

....

h) Are you going to take the exam next week?

....

i) Are you going to work very hard in the autumn?

....

k) When are you going to write to Mrs Brown?

....

l) Where are you going to travel?

....

27.

Translate into English:

a) Nächstes Jahr fahre ich nach England.

....

b) Ich hoffe, daß das Wetter gut sein wird.

....

c) Wenn es regnet, bleibe ich die meiste Zeit in London.

....

d) Ich habe vor, meinen Brieffreund Andrew zu besuchen.

....

e) Er wird im August 17 Jahre alt.

....

f) Heute abend treffe ich meine Freundin Jean.

....

g) Komme bitte nicht um 9 Uhr. Wir haben dann eine Konferenz.

....

h) Werden Sie morgen arbeiten?

....

i) Ich werde morgen sehr schwer arbeiten.

....

k) Morgen wird die Sonne scheinen.

....

l) Herr Brown wird sein Haus so bald als möglich verkaufen.

....

28.

Hier war der Fehlerteufel am Werk. Verbessere bitte alle Fehler aus Schülerarbeiten:

a) Frau Green fährt nächste Woche nach Paris.
Mrs Green travels to Paris next week.

....

b) Sie hofft, daß ihr Mann mitfährt.
She hopes that her husband travels with her.

....

c) In den Ferien werden wir nicht im Klassenzimmer sitzen.
In the holidays we won't be sit in class.

....

d) Ich besuche dich, bevor ich nach London abfahre.
I'll come and see you before I shall leave for London.

....

e) Peter wird die Prüfung bestehen, wenn er die richtigen Antworten weiß.
Peter is going to pass the exam, if he knows the correct answers.

....

f) Ich erwarte, daß Billy morgen kommt.
I expect Billy comes tomorrow.

....

29.

Comprehension Test: A Letter From Peter

I. Give the correct forms of the verbs:

Dear Ian,

You .... (be) surprised .... (get) a letter from London.

I .... (be) here for over three weeks now. You ....

(know) that an uncle of mine .... (live) here. Last winter he ....

(invite) me .... (spend) my summer holidays in England. Uncle Rupert

.... (have) a small car, and he .... (allow) me ....

(use) it. Fortunately, I .... (pass) my driving test some time ago, and

.... (get) my driving licence. In the past few weeks I ....

.... (already + do) a lot of sightseeing. But there are a few places I

.... (not see + yet).

When I .... (arrive) here my uncle .... (congratulate)

me on my English. .... (you, remember) my problems with

English at school? Uncle Rupert .... (suggest) that I

.... (write) to you in English.

I hope .... (see) you soon.

Peter

34

II. Cross the correct translation:

a) Peters Onkel lebt seit zwanzig Jahren in England.
   - ☐ Peter's uncle lives in England for 20 years.
   - ☐ Peter's uncle lived in England for 20 years.
   - ☐ Peter's uncle has lived in England for 20 years.

b) Er hilft seiner Frau jeden Tag bei der Hausarbeit.
   - ☐ Every day he helps his wife with the housework.
   - ☐ Every day he is helping his wife with the housework.
   - ☐ Every day he has helped his wife with the housework.

c) Letzten Samstag ging er einkaufen für sie.
   - ☐ Last Saturday he has gone shopping for her.
   - ☐ Last Suturday he was going shopping for her.
   - ☐ Last Saturday he went shopping for her.

d) Mein Onkel las gerade ein Buch, als ich ankam.
   - ☐ My uncle was just reading a book, when I arrived.
   - ☐ My uncle read a book, when I was arriving.
   - ☐ My uncle had just read a book when I arrived.

e) Nachdem ich eine Woche in London verbracht hatte, fuhr ich nach Dover.
   - ☐ After I have spent a week in London, I went to Dover.
   - ☐ After I had spent a week in London, I went to Dover.
   - ☐ After I spent a week in London, I had gone to Dover.

f) Nächstes Jahr besuche ich Onkel Rupert wieder.
   - ☐ Next year I shall visit Uncle Rupert again.
   - ☐ Next year I visit Uncle Rupert again.
   - ☐ Next year I am visiting Uncle Rupert again.

Kapitel 3

Hilfsverben (Auxiliaries)

30.
Lernhilfen für die Übungen.
Besonderheiten:

Tom speak**s** English. He **can** speak German too.	**Kein -s!**
Do you speak French? **Can** you speak French?	**Frage ohne do/does/did!**
We don't speak Spanish. We **can't** speak Spanish.	**Verneinung ohne do/does/did!**
You promised to come, **did**n't you? We **ought to** go, **oughtn't** we?	**Sie bleiben bei den "tags"!**
Tom hoped **to win**. He hoped **to be allowed to** come.	**Kein Infinitiv!** Du brauchst eine Ersatzform: <u>to be allowed to</u> für <u>may</u>!
I **must** walk home. Yesterday I **had** to walk too. Tomorrow I'**ll have to** walk too.	**Fehlende Zeitformen** werden mit Ersatzformen (= Substitutes) gebildet!

Grundbedeutungen:

May I come in? (Darf?) **Might** I use your pen? (Dürfte?) How often **were** you **allowed to** go out? (hast dürfen?)	**may** bezeichnet die **Erlaubnis:** **dürfen** Fehlende Formen bildest du mit **to be allowed to!**
He **may** come tomorrow. (= kommt vielleicht; kann kommen) He **might** come tomorrow. (= Es könnte sein, daß . . .)	**may** bezeichnet die **Möglichkeit:** **vielleicht sein**

Can we park here? (Dürfen?) **Could** you park there? (Durftest?)	**can** bezeichnet die **Erlaubnis:** **dürfen**
You **can** play here. The room is empty. (Es ist möglich, daß . . .)	**can** bezeichnet die **Möglichkeit:** **können, möglicherweise sein**
Mr Brown **can** speak German well. We **were able to** catch the train. (= konnten)	**can** bezeichnet die **Fähigkeit:** **können, fähig sein** Fehlende Formen bildest du mit **to be able to!**

You **must** get up earlier. I **had to** get up earlier. (mußte)	**must** bezeichnet die **Notwendigkeit** oder den Zwang: **müssen** Fehlende Formen bildest du mit **to have to!**
Tom **must** be home now. (Es ist sicher, daß . . .) You **must** come to our party. (Du mußt aber . . .)	**must** bezeichnet die **Gewißheit und Wahrscheinlichkeit: müssen, sicher sein** **must** bezeichnet die **Aufforderung:**

31.

Use 'must' or 'may' to transform the sentences:

Example: Tom <u>will perhaps</u> come.   <u>I'm sure</u> Tom <u>is</u> at home.

          Tom <u>may</u> come.   Tom <u>must be</u> at home.

a) Perhaps I'm wrong, but I think I know this man.

    ....

b) I'm sure your English book is at home.

    Your English book ....

c) Ian is certainly happy now that he has got a good job.

    ....

d) Possibly the match will take place in the big stadium.

    ....

e) This is probably the car we have been looking for.

    ....

f) The man with the red skin is certainly an Indian.

    ....

g) I'm sure Tom is fed up with his Maths homework.

    ....

h) Perhaps Janet and Sam will go to Norway next summer.

    ....

i) Possibly the teacher is wrong.

    ....

k) This is probably the letter I received from Mr Traynor.

    ....

l) Billy is certainly happy to have passed his exam.

    ....

32.

Cross the correct translation:

a) It may be raining, take an umbrella with you.
   ☐ Es wird regnen, nimm einen Schirm mit.
   ☐ Es wird vielleicht regnen, nimm einen Schirm mit.
   ☐ Es muß regnen, nimm einen Schirm mit.

b) Sam asked if he might go to the match on Saturday.
   ☐ Sam fragte, ob er am Samstag zum Spiel gehen dürfe.
   ☐ Sam fragte, ob er am Samstag zum Spiel gehen müsse.
   ☐ Sam fragte, ob er am Samstag zum Spiel gehen solle.

c) Might I have a glass of water, please?
   ☐ Möchte ich vielleicht ein Glas Wasser haben?
   ☐ Kann ich bitte ein Glas Wasser haben?
   ☐ Könnte ich vielleicht ein Glas Wasser haben?

d) Jimmy has not been able to translate the text.
   ☐ Jimmy kann den Text nicht übersetzen.
   ☐ Jimmy ist nicht in der Lage, den Text zu übersetzen.
   ☐ Jimmy hat den Text nicht übersetzen können.

e) Could I come in for a moment?
   ☐ Konnte ich für einen Augenblick hereinkommen?
   ☐ Könnte ich für einen Augenblick hereinkommen?
   ☐ Habe ich für einen Augenblick hereinkommen können?

f) You may shut the window.
   ☐ Sie dürfen das Fenster schließen.
   ☐ Sie könnten das Fenster schließen.
   ☐ Sie müssen das Fenster schließen.

g) You'll have to study harder, if you want to pass the exam.
   ☐ Du wirst fleißiger studieren, wenn du die Prüfung bestehen willst.
   ☐ Du wirst fleißiger werden, wenn du die Prüfung bestehen willst.
   ☐ Du wirst fleißiger studieren müssen, wenn du die Prüfung bestehen willst.

33.

Use other tenses:

a) Diana **must** get up at seven.

Yesterday she .... at six.

Tomorrow she .... at nine.

b) Janet **must** help in the kitchen.

How long .... last Sunday?

c) Tony **can** play cricket very well.

When .... Bob .... to play it just as well?

d) Mr Miller **can** drive a car.

His wife .... a car as soon as she has passed her driving test.

e) No-one **may** enter the stadium without a ticket today.

Next Saturday everyone .... the stadium.

Last Sunday only children .... the stadium.

f) Today the mechanic **must** repair a car.

Yesterday he .... a motorbike.

g) "**May** I go out tonight?"

Last night Sammy ....

h) "I **can** pay you back the money you lent me."

But I .... to pay you back before today.

40

34.

Lernhilfen für die Übungen.
Erweiterung der Grundmuster:

Need we ask? I don't think we **need** go to the party.	**need** drückt eine **Notwendigkeit** aus: **müssen, brauchen**
We **need not** wait any longer. We **don't have to** wait. (= We **haven't got to** wait.) We **didn't have to** come early.	**need not: nicht müssen** **nicht zu brauchen** Du verwendest für fehlende Formen: **not to have to** (= Wir mußten nicht)
Children **must not** play here. You **can't** park here. They **are not allowed to** play here. We **were not allowed to** go.	**must not** + **can't** drücken ein **Verbot** aus: **nicht dürfen** Fehlende Formen ersetzt du durch **not to be allowed to** (= Wir durften nicht)
Shall we go? You **should** get up earlier. You **ought to** get up earlier. Each player **is to wear** the same shirts. (= **soll**) He **is said** to have stolen a car.	**shall** wird in der **Frage** (bei: I und we) verwendet: **soll? sollen?** **should** + **ought to** drücken einen **Rat** bzw. eine **Verpflichtung** aus! (= Du solltest) **to be to** drückt eine **Anordnung** aus: **sollen!** Mit **is said to** drückst du eine **Vermutung** aus: **soll** angeblich
He **may have** forgotten the book. He **can't have** arrived yet. You **must have** misunderstood me. He **should have** come earlier.	Er **hat** das Buch **vielleicht** vergessen. Er **kann unmöglich** schon da sein. Du **mußt** mich falsch verstanden **haben**. Er **hätte** früher kommen **sollen**.

35.

Translate into English:

a) Sollen wir mit Barbara und Hannes Tennis spielen?

....

b) Der Bus sollte um 5 Uhr fahren, aber er kam zu spät.

....

c) Ich habe ihn verpaßt. Was soll ich jetzt tun?

....

d) Ich soll um 5 Uhr abreisen.

....

e) Ich hätte den früheren Zug nehmen sollen.

....

f) Du solltest es ihm erzählen.

....

g) Sie hätten ihn nicht allein lassen sollen.

....

h) Es sollte nicht wieder vorkommen.

....

i) Wenn ich von Peter hören sollte, werde ich es ihnen sagen.

....

k) Es hätte längst geschehen sollen.

....

l) Nächste Woche werden wir mit dem Rad fahren müssen.

....

36.
Choose the correct form:

a) Tom ☐ needn't   forget to feed his dog when he goes out.
         ☐ mustn't
         ☐ won't have to

b) Judy ☐ mustn't   wash up when she has some homework to do.
         ☐ needn't
         ☐ didn't have to

c) If Hannes had learnt more, he ☐ wouldn't have had   to repeat
                               ☐ needn't have to
                               ☐ mustn't

    the test.

d) The bikes ☐ needn't   be parked in front of the school.
              ☐ don't have to
              ☐ mustn't

e) ☐ Mustn't they   walk a long way after they had missed the train?
   ☐ Didn't they have to
   ☐ Needn't they

f) He ☐ mustn't   have left so early. There is plenty of time.
       ☐ needn't
       ☐ didn't have to

g) You ☐ mustn't stay   if you don't want to.
        ☐ needn't stay
        ☐ won't have to stay

h) Mr Broke has no money. He ☐ mustn't have bought such a big car.
                               ☐ needn't buy
                               ☐ didn't have to buy

37.

**Hier war wieder der Fehlerteufel am Werk!
Verbessere bitte alle Schülerfehler:**

a) Der Zug kann noch nicht angekommen sein.
The train cannot arrive yet.

....

b) Du mußt nicht länger warten.
You must not wait any longer.

....

c) Tom sollte um 8 Uhr am Bahnhof sein.
Tom must be at the station at eight.

....

d) Bill wird zum Bahnhof gehen müssen, um seinen Koffer zu holen.
Billy will must go to the station to get his suitcase.

....

e) Hannes mußte den nächsten Zug nehmen.
Hannes must took the next train.

....

f) Mr Smith durfte den Hund nicht mit in den Supermarkt nehmen.
Mr Smith might not take the dog into the supermarket.

....

g) Wenn Utes Fahrrad in Ordnung gewesen wäre, hätte sie zur Schule fahren können.
If Ute's bike had been in order, she can have drived to school.

....

h) Die Mädchen mußten nicht abwaschen.
The girls had not to wash up.

....

44

38.
Comprehension Test: An Adventure

When Tom's parents went away for a day, the boys just had to do something. How could they miss such a chance?

So Tom asked his friends if they could come. He was not allowed to use his moped, but they were able to go all the way by bike. They wanted to cycle to the river, where they intended to light a fire. Nobody would be able to forbid that this time. When their parents had been with them, they had never been allowed to do that. They had to return in time because their parents weren't to know anything about their trip.

They would have come back, if they had been able to. But one of the bikes had been stolen, and so they had to phone Tom's father to get them home in his van.

I. Write complete sentences (The text will help you):

a) Tom .... ask his father before he uses the moped.

b) Tom asked his friends if they .... come.

c) It had been a long way, but they .... to go by bike.

d) .... they miss such a chance?

e) Tom .... ride a bike, but he .... to drive a car.

f) When their parents are with them, they .... to light a fire.

g) "You .... be right, but why .... I .... to use my moped?" Tom asked his father.

45

II. Form the negative with "not":

a) Tim may use his moped, but Tom .... use his moped.

b) Mr Miller can drive a car, but Tom .... drive a car.

c) Tony must help in the garden, but Tom .... help.

d) Tony is able to run 20 miles, but Tom .... to run 5 miles.

e) Tony will be allowed to go camping in his holidays, but Tom .... to go camping.

f) Tony could have walked home, but Tom .... because he hurt his foot.

III. Form sentences (Mind the forms):

a) We / must / help / our friends / last week

....

b) You / must not / go out / last night

....

c) We / may / visit / Susy / next Sunday

....

d) Tony / can / do / the exercises / next week

....

e) The headmaster / must / be informed / yesterday

....

IV. Translate into German:

a) The boys from 8c must have done it.

....

b) Couldn't they apologize?

....

c) Could father have helped the boys?

....

d) They ought to be quiet.

....

e) They ought to have been ashamed of themselves.

....

f) Tom had had to phone several times, before his father came.

....

g) He should have asked his parents.

....

h) They might have allowed him to take the moped this time.

....

i) The boys needn't have been afraid.

....

k) We must not forget to come home in time.

....

l) They simply could not miss the chance.

....

m) Tony hadn't been allowed to light a fire.

....

Kapitel 4

Passiv (The Passive, Leideform)

39.
Lernhilfen für die Übungen.
Bildung und Formen:

English **is spoken** all over the world. America **was discovered** in 1492. ↑ ↑ **to be + Past Participle**	Das Passiv wird gebildet aus einer Form von **to be** und dem Partizip Perfekt (**third form of the verb**; **Past Participle**)! → **22**
The comedy was written **by Shakespeare.** The burglar has been caught **by the police.** ↑ ↑ **by + agent**	Der **Urheber (agent)** der Handlung kann angeführt werden, wenn es von Interesse ist!

Häufige Fehler:

a) Die Regeln für die Zeitstufen sind dieselben wie bei Aktivsätzen.
   Beachte also Signalwörter oder den Satzzusammenhang!
b) Verwende bei Umformungen vom Aktiv ins Passiv die gleiche Zeit!

40.
Complete the translation:

a) English .... all over the world.
   (Englisch **wird** überall auf der Welt **gesprochen**.)

b) The play .... by Shakespeare.
   (Das Stück **wurde** von Shakespeare **geschrieben**.)

c) The burglar .... by the police.
   (Der Einbrecher **ist** von der Polizei **gefangen worden**.)

d) The letter ....
   (Der Brief **war geschrieben worden**.)

e) The conference .... by the President.
   (Die Konferenz **wird** vom Präsidenten **eröffnet werden**.)

f) The conference .... by the President if he had more time.
   (Die Konferenz **würde** vom Präsidenten **eröffnet werden**, ...)

g) The decision .... by Monday.
   (Die Entscheidung **wird** bis Montag **getroffen worden sein**.)

h) The decision .... if Mr Brown had agreed.
   (Die Entscheidung **wäre getroffen worden**, ...)

i) The new road ....
   (Die neue Straße **wird gerade gebaut**.)

k) The conference ....
   (Die Konferenz **wurde gerade abgehalten**.)

l) The window ....
   (Das Fenster **muß geschlossen werden**.)

41.

Complete the sentences:

Example: My desk is not in its place.

It has been removed. (Use the Present Perfect!)

a) Ten thousand pounds .... (steal) at the bank.

b) This letter .... (write) perfectly.

c) Mr Brown's car .... (repair) at the garage.

d) I hope only correct answers .... (give).

e) The quarrel between Mr Brown and his wife .... (settle).

f) All their problems .... (solve).

g) A lot of work .... (do) today.

h) This room .... (not, clean) for weeks.

i) My friend lost his bike. It .... (not, find) yet.

k) Smoking in schools .... (not, allow) for some years.

l) Up to the present Atlantis .... (not, discover).

m) The Millers' dog .... (run over) by a car.

n) Angela .... (never, invite) to a party.

o) These English books are very dirty. They .... (use) by too many pupils.

42.
Make sentences in the passive:

a) English .... (understand) all over the world.

b) Angela .... (invite) to our party next week.

c) A thriller .... (show) on TV last night.

d) A lot of money .... (earn) in professional football.

e) The match .... (win) by our team next Sunday.

f) The Browns' house .... (build) twenty years ago.

g) The new building .... (not, finish) yet.

h) Our new school .... (finish) by next summer.

i) This problem .... (discuss) by our headmaster tomorrow.

k) German .... (not, teach) in all English schools.

l) After the accident a lot of questions .... (ask) by the police.

m) Great progress .... (make) in computer techniques in recent years.

n) Last year a rocket .... (send) to Venus.

o) England .... (conquer) by William I.

43.
Lernhilfen für die Übungen.
Unterschiede zum Deutschen:

Mrs. Brown **was helped**.
She   **was helped**.
(Somebody helped her.)

Man half Frau Brown.
Man half ihr.

Alle transitiven Verben können im Englischen den Passiv bilden, auch wenn es im Deutschen nicht möglich ist!

The children must be **looked after**.
Somebody must **look   after** them.

Verb + Preposition!

Verb + Präposition bleiben auch im Passiv zusammen!

(Somebody sent **me the book**.)

1. / 2. Objekt!
I was sent the book.

Der Aktivsatz hat zwei Objekte! Beide könnten Subjekt des Passivsatzes werden! Üblich ist nur die **persönliche Form!**
(Man schickte mir . . .)

44.
Use a personal subject when you put these sentences into the passive:

a) Someone showed **me** how to open this tin.

....

b) Somebody has already paid the mechanic for the material.

....

c) They asked the reporter to leave the room.

....

d) They gave Mr Brown a lesson.

....

e) They will give every child a reward.

....

45.
Use a passive infinitive construction:

a) You can shut the door.

....

b) You should wash the car.

....

c) They must take the books to the library.

....

d) They ought to tidy their room.

....

e) They could not see the mountains.

....

46.
Agent or not?

a) We use this room only when we have guests.

....

b) Lord Byron wrote the poem.

....

c) We must look after them.

....

d) We must look after grandmother.

....

e) They dealt with the matter correctly.

....

f) The pupils broke the windows on the first floor.

....

g) Someone could have stopped the train.

....

h) Thieves stole the diamonds.

....

i) People say that the Browns have bought a new house.

....

k) Her father gave Susy a wonderful watch.

....

l) They will have to pull down the old house.

....

47.

Translate into English:

a) Mein Fahrrad ist gestohlen worden.

....

b) Hier wird gerade ein neues Kino gebaut.

....

c) Die Arbeit wurde sehr sorgfältig vorbereitet.

....

d) Der Supermarkt wird im nächsten Monat eröffnet werden.

....

e) Der Musiker wurde von den Leuten willkommen geheißen.

....

f) Billys Armbanduhr wird gerade repariert.

....

48.

Translate "man":

a) Was soll man tun?

....

b) Das hätte man besser machen können.

....

c) Man erzählte mir die Geschichte.

....

d) Man kann diese Bücher im Supermarkt kaufen.

....

e) Man muß Ute sofort schreiben.

....

49.
Comprehension Test: Doing The Housework

When Janet and Sam leave the house in the morning, Mrs Burns waves to them.
At nine she dusts and sweeps the dining-room. Then she takes the vaccuum
cleaner and cleans the hall, the study and the staircase. The children's rooms are
in a mess, and she must put them in order.
At eleven she must prepare the meal. Today she is frying fish in a pan, and boiling
potatoes in a pot. Little Bob and his friends are playing outside. They are making
a lot of noise.
At half past twelve Janet comes home from school, goes upstairs and does her
room. Then she helps Mother in the kitchen.
Tom sometimes lays the table, and after dinner he clears it.

I. Look at the text and complete the sentences:

a) The dining-room .... and .... by

....

b) The table .... by ....

c) The children's rooms .... by ....

d) A lot of noise .... by ....

e) Janet's room .... at half past twelve.

f) Fish .... in a ....

g) Potatoes .... in a ....

h) The meal.................................. at eleven.

i) Mother .... in the kitchen by ....

56

II. Turn into the passive:

a) They sent for the doctor

....

b) The nurse looked after the children.

....

c) They sent the children away.

....

d) Someone has written on the table.

....

e) The children always laugh at Tim.

....

f) Has anyone ever thought about that problem?

....

g) People say that he has stolen a car.

....

h) People know that she is an honest woman.

....

i) People believe that he is living in America.

....

k) They will never speak about this problem again.

....

l) You can read these books quite easily.

....

m) The tourists must pay for the hotel in dollars.

....

III. Hier hat der Fehlerteufel wieder sein Unwesen getrieben! Verbessere alle Fehler aus Schüler-arbeiten:

a) The rooms are always sweeped by Mother.

....

b) The staircase is cleaning with the vaccuum cleaner.

....

....

c) The fish is being frying in a pan.

....

d) The new potatoes will be plant in spring.

....

e) Buses are drove by bus-drivers.

....

f) All kinds of food can bought at a supermarket.

....

g) Cold drinks must be keeping in a fridge.

....

h) The police was caught by the burglar.

....

i) Shorts and T-shirts is worn in summer.

....

58

IV. Translate into German:

a) Mrs Cartor was offered a job

b) Mr Thomson was thanked for the wonderful present.

c) I was allowed to go home because I felt sick.

d) K. Keegan is said to be an excellent footballer.

e) Last night the doctor was sent for.

f) When the boys were playing football yesterday, Tim was being laughed at.

g) The team will be offered a great chance.

h) This watch can be repaired easily.

i) He is supposed to fly to Paris next week.

k) It was said that Mr Brown would find another house.

Kapitel 5

Konditionalsätze (Conditional Clauses, if-Clauses, Bedingungssätze)

50.
Lernhilfen für die Übungen.
Grundmuster:

If he **works** hard, Tom **will pass** his exam. | Hier sind Bedingung (If . . .) und Folgerung **realistisch!** (Er lernt tüchtig!)

↑ **Present** **if-Clause** ↑ **Future** **Main Clause**

If he **worked** hard, Tom **would pass** his exam. | Hier ist es **unwahrscheinlich,** daß die Bedingung (If . . .) erfüllt wird! (Er lernt derzeit nicht so tüchtig!)

↑ **Past** **if-Clause** ↑ **Conditional** **Main Clause**

If he **had worked** hard, Tom **would have passed** his exam.

↑ **Past Perfect** **if-Clause** ↑ **Conditional Perfect** **Main Clause** | Hier ist die Bedingung nicht mehr zu erfüllen, da die Sache **anders verlief!** (Er hat es nicht geschafft!)

Erweiterung:

If he works hard, Tom will pass his exam.
Tom will pass his exam, **if he works hard**. | Beide Stellungen sind in allen Zeiten möglich!

If I **was** oder: If I **were**
If he **was** oder: If he **were** | Beide Formen sind bei 'I' bzw. 'he, she, it' möglich!

51.

Make sentences which are similar to the example:

Example: Tom / work hard / pass / exam
   If Tom works hard, he will pass his exam.

a) Mr Brown / run / catch / train

....

b) Mr Brown / send / address / I / answer / letter

....

c) it / not rain / I / take / it / post-office

....

d) they / work fast / Mr Brown / have / tomorrow / it

....

e) letter / arrive / tomorrow / Mr Brown / be / very happy

....

Example: Tom / work hard / pass / exam
   If Tom worked hard, he would pass his exam.

f) Peter / have / enough money / drive / to London

....

g) Mrs Brown / have more time / buy / dress

....

h) Mr Brown / have / opportunity / buy / new suit

....

i) Peter / hit / dog / bite / him

....

k) Somebody / help / me / be / easier / it

....

Example: Tom / pass / exam / work / harder
Tom would have passed his exam, if he had worked harder.

l) Our team / not lose / match / train / harder

....

m) Our class / win / prize / not be / so stupid

....

n) Mr Crash / pass / driving test / not be / so lazy

....

o) You / improve / English / go to England / earlier

....

p) Driver / not skid / not drive / so fast

....

r) Peter / enjoy / party more / not drink / so much

....

52.
Put the verbs in brackets into the correct tense:

a) Tom .... (go) to the concert, if he can afford it.

b) Tom .... (go) to the theatre, if he could afford it.

c) More people .... (travel) by underground,

if the fares .... (be) cheaper. Unfortunately they aren't.

d) .... (you, accept) this book, if I buy it?

e) If I had seen you, I .... (wait).

f) Mrs Brown .... (understand) M. Blanc,

if he .... (speak) more slowly. Unfortunately he has left.

53.

Hier war wieder der Fehlerteufel am Werk!
Verbessere bitte alle Fehler aus Schülerarbeiten:

a) Herr Brown würde dir helfen, wenn du ihn fragen würdest.
Mr Brown would help you, if you would ask him.

....

b) Wenn Tom eher gekommen wäre, hätten wir Karten gespielt.
If Tom would have come earlier, we would have played cards.

....

c) Ich spreche nicht mit dir, wenn du dich nicht entschuldigst.
I don't speak to you again, if you don't apologize.

....

d) Was würdest du tun, wenn du viel Geld hättest?
What did you do, if you would have a lot of money?

....

e) Was hättest du getan, wenn du letzten Sommer in England gewesen wärst?
What would you have done, if you have been in England last summer?

....

f) Wenn ich Ferien mache, reise ich nach Schottland.
If I go on holiday, I travel to Scotland.

....

54.
Lernhilfen für die Übungen.
Erweiterung der Grundmuster:

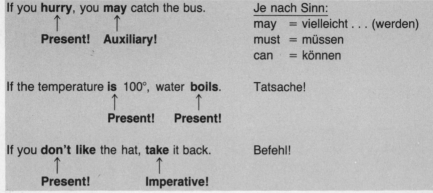

If you **hurry**, you **may** catch the bus.

  ↑   ↑

  Present! Auxiliary!

Je nach Sinn:
may = vielleicht . . . (werden)
must = müssen
can = können

If the temperature **is** 100°, water **boils**.

  ↑   ↑

  Present! Present!

Tatsache!

If you **don't like** the hat, **take** it back.

  ↑   ↑

  Present! Imperative!

Befehl!

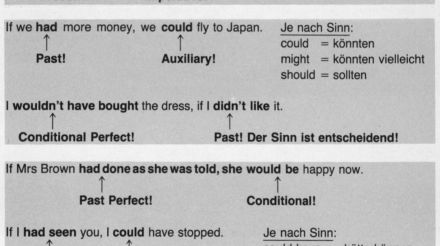

If we **had** more money, we **could** fly to Japan.

  ↑   ↑

  Past!   Auxiliary!

Je nach Sinn:
could = könnten
might = könnten vielleicht
should = sollten

I **wouldn't have bought** the dress, if I **didn't like** it.

  ↑   ↑

  Conditional Perfect!   Past! Der Sinn ist entscheidend!

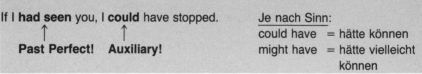

If Mrs Brown **had done as she was told, she would be** happy now.

  ↑   ↑

  Past Perfect! Conditional!

If I **had seen** you, I **could** have stopped.

  ↑   ↑

  Past Perfect! Auxiliary!

Je nach Sinn:
could have = hätte können
might have = hätte vielleicht
                    können

55.

Complete:

a) You can switch off the radio, if you .... (not like) the programme.

b) If you miss the bus, you .... (can, not, come) in time.

c) You .... (must, stay) in bed, if you .... (be) ill.

d) If Tom worked harder, he .... (may, pass) his exam.

e) We could catch the bus, if we .... (run) all the way.

f) If every player had played well, we .... (can, win) the match.

g) A bad accident .... (may, happen), if Mr Brown had not driven so carefully.

h) If you want to become rich, you .... (must, earn) money.

i) Tom would be happy, if Christine .... (be) at his party.

k) You .... (must, not, go out), unless your father gives you permission.

l) The children .... (can, not, read), if there is no light in their room.

56.

Translate into German:

a) If I were you, I would buy a new bike.

....

b) If he runs, Bill will be at school in time.

....

c) If he runs, Bill may be at school in time.

....

d) If you are in a hurry, you can take my bike.

....

e) I'll go home now, unless you need me.

....

f) If you don't know the way, you can ask a policeman.

....

g) You can take my bike, provided that you bring it back safely.

....

h) You needn't go by bus, if the weather is fine.

....

i) We could have seen the mountains, if there hadn't been so many clouds.

....

k) Do you think we might have had more fun, if Betty and George had been with us?

....

l) If only Bill would stop talking all the time.

....

57.

a) Wenn du dich beeilst, kannst du den Zug um 7 Uhr erreichen.

....

b) Wenn du dich beeilst, könntest du den Zug um 6.45 erreichen.

....

c) Wenn du einen Reisepaß hast, kannst du in die meisten Länder reisen.

....

d) Wenn du in die USA reisen willst, mußt du ein Visa haben.

....

e) Wenn die Sonne nicht scheint, ist es sehr kalt.

....

f) Wenn du nach Italien reisen willst, solltest du etwas Italienisch können.

....

g) Wenn ich mehr Zeit hätte, würde ich ein Buch lesen.

....

h) Wenn ich du wäre, würde ich zu Hause bleiben.

....

i) Wenn du eher gekommen wärst, wären wir jetzt fertig.

....

k) Wenn du mich angerufen hättest, hätte ich dir helfen können.

....

l) Wenn du mich gefragt hättest, hätte ich dir vielleicht helfen können.

....

58.
Lernhilfen für die Übungen.
Höfliche Bitten:

If you **will** wait, I'll call the manager.   Beachte:
   = wollten   **will** bzw. **would** im if-Satz!

If you **would** wait, I'll call him at once.
   = bitte wollten

I'd be pleased if you **would** answer soon.
        = bitte wollten

I'd be grateful if you **could** come again.
        = könnten

I'd be happy if you **would like** to come with me.
I'd be happy if you **would care** to come with me.

59.

Completo:

a) If you .... (wait) a moment, I'll ask a policeman.

b) Tony .... (be) pleased, if his friend would help him with his homework.

c) I should be very grateful, if you .... (post) the letter today.

d) Bob's father would be thankful, if the children .... (help) him to wash his car.

e) I would be glad, if you .... (lend) me the book.

60.

Translate into English:

a) Ich würde mich freuen, wenn du eher kommen würdest.

....

b) Wenn Sie einen Augenblick warten wollten, rufe ich meinen Vater.

....

....

c) Herr Brown wäre sehr dankbar, wenn sein Auto repariert würde.

....

d) Ich wäre sehr froh, wenn du länger bleiben könntest.

....

61.

Hier war wieder der Fehlerteufel am Werk!
Verbessere bitte alle Fehler aus Schüler-arbeiten:

a) If Klaus would ask his father, he would allow him to go to Scotland.

....

....

b) If I am Klaus, I would go to a travel office.

....

c) If his brother has time, he will have gone to Scotland, too.

....

d) Ian's parents would be glad, if their son stays at home.

....

e) The boys might fly to Aberdeen, if they have enough money.

....

f) If you don't like camping, go you to a hotel.

....

g) If the boys come to Scotland, they will can stay with Ian.

....

h) If Ian would have known his friend's plans, he wouldn't have gone to Russia.

....

....

62.
Comprehension Test: Where Would You Like To Go?

If you could choose, where would you like to spend your holidays? Would you like to go to Britain or to Italy? The question is whether you prefer to stay at a hotel or guest house or go camping.

If you wanted to visit Britain, you should take your car with you. Going by car gives you a good chance not only to see the big towns, like London or Glasgow, but to find nice places in the country. If you wanted to get away from the noisy tourist centres, you could go to one of the little villages in the Highlands or perhaps in the Yorkshire Moors. You can go walking or fishing in one of the rivers. If you come in August, you'll certainly have good weather in Scotland. When you are in Scotland, you should visit Edinburgh, of course. You must go to a travel office if you plan a holiday in Britain. The travel agent will tell you everything you have to do before you leave.

I. Answer in complete sentences:

a) What should you do, if you wanted to visit Britain?

....

b) What could you do, if you wanted to get away from the noisy tourist centres?

....

c) What will the weather be like, if you come in August?

....

d) What should you do when you are in Scotland?

....

e) What must you do, if you plan a journey to Britain?

....

II. Cross the correct answer:

a) If Klaus has enough time, he ☐ would visit his friend.
  ☐ will visit
  ☐ visits

b) His friend Ian would stay at home, if he ☐ knew
  ☐ would know
  ☐ knows

that Klaus would be there.

c) "Klaus, if you come to Scotland, you ☐ go   and see Edinburgh."
  ☐ will go
  ☐ must go

d) "You ☐ can say   that you know Scotland, unless you have seen
  ☐ won't be able to say
  ☐ wouldn't be able to say

Loch Ness."

e) "I would be grateful if you ☐ send   me a book about your country."
  ☐ will send
  ☐ would send

f) "My parents ☐ would be glad,   if you would come in August."
  ☐ will be glad,
  ☐ would have been glad,

g) "If you had come last year, we ☐ will have seen   the Edinburgh
  ☐ could see
  ☐ could have seen

Festival."

III.

Translate into English:

a) Jean würde sich freuen, wenn Klaus nach Schottland kommen könnte.

....

b) Wenn Klaus sein Taschengeld spart, kann er die Reise bezahlen.

....

c) Klaus hätte schon letztes Jahr fahren können, wenn er nicht krank geworden wäre.

....

....

d) "Klaus, wenn du nicht kommen kannst, sag' es uns rechtzeitig."

....

e) "Wenn der Flug nach Edinburgh zu teuer ist, fahr' mit der Eisenbahn."

....

f) "Ich wäre sehr froh, wenn du mir ein Buch über Schottland schicken würdest."

....

....

g) "Ich wäre auch dankbar, wenn mein Bruder mitkommen könnte."

....

h) "Wenn wir Zeit haben, werden wir dich am Bahnhof oder Flugplatz abholen."

....

Kapitel 6

Adjektive (Adjectives, Eigenschaftswörter)

63.
Lernhilfen für die Übungen.
Bildung der Steigerungsformen:

	Comparative	Superlative	
old	old**er**	old**est**	Du hängst **-er** bzw. **-est** an bei **einsilbigen** und
easy	easi**er**	easi**est**	**zweisilbigen** Adjektiven
holy	holi**er**	holi**est**	auf -y, -ly, -le und -er!
simple	simpl**er**	simpl**est**	
clever	clever**er**	clever**est**	
careful	**more** careful	**most** careful	Du stellst **more** bzw. **most** voran bei den anderen **zweisilbigen** sowie bei
important	**more** important	**most** important	**allen drei-** und mehr-
intelligent	**more** intelligent	**most** intelligent	silbigen Adjektiven!

Sonderformen:

good	better	best	auch: much/many –
bad + ill	worse	worst	more – most; little –
far	farther	farthest	less – least!
	further	furthest	

Schreibregeln:

easy	easier	easiest	**y** wird **i**!
big	bigger	biggest	Konsonant **verdoppelt**!
fin**e**	finer	finest	**-e** fällt weg!

Verwendung:

Mrs Brown **is** a friendly lady.	Adjektiv nach **to be** und ähnlichen
She **looks** very nice.	Verben und wenn über ein Substantiv
She **sweeps** the floor clean.	oder Pronomen ausgesagt wird!

→ 82

64.

Give the comparative and superlative forms of these adjectives:

attractive ....

beautiful ....

charming ....

difficult ....

expensive ....

fat ....

good ....

happy ....

interesting ....

low ....

much ....

nice ....

pretty ....

tasty ....

ugly ....

wonderful ....

young ....

65.

Fill in the correct forms:

a) Susy is the .... (pretty) girl around.

b) Barbara is the .... (beautiful) girl in town.

c) Bill is the .... (clever) boy in our class.

d) Jane is the .... (intelligent) girl in our class.

e) Mr Root is the .... (good) dentist in town.

f) Mr Crash is the .... (bad) pilot in the country.

g) Mrs Brown's .... (old) daughter is only six.

h) The .... (old) inhabitant of our town is 107.

i) The .... (near) disco is ten miles away.

k) The .... (near) train to London leaves in 5 minutes.

l) Mr Brown wants to get .... (far) information.

m) The last lesson was the .... (little) interesting of all.

n) It was the .... (bad) summer in fifty years.

o) It was the .... (much) interesting film I've ever seen.

p) You can read the .... (late) news in the newspapers.

q) Mrs Brown always wears the .... (late) fashion.

r) This is the .... (late) sentence of the exercise!!!!

76

66.

Lernhilfen für die Übungen.
Vergleich im Satz:

Mr Brown is **as** old **as** Mr Black. = **so** alt **wie**
Mr Green is **not so** old **as** Mr White. = **nicht so** alt **wie**

Mrs Brown is **older than** Mrs Black. = **älter als**
A car is **more expensive than** a bike. = **teurer als**

The nearest disco is ten miles away. = **Die nächste ...**
The most difficult question was No. 10. = **Die schwierigste ...**

Übersetzungstraining:

The sooner you come, **the** better.
Je eher du kommst, **desto** besser.

Susan's German is getting **better and better.**
Susannes Deutsch wird **immer besser.**

Our tests are becoming **more and more difficult**.
Unsere Tests werden **immer schwieriger**.
↓

Mr Brown asked **a most** interesting question.
Herr B. stellte **eine höchst** interessante Frage.
↓

This was **the most interesting** question of all.
Dies war **die interessanteste** Frage von allen.

Peter's French is **much** better than mine.
P.s Französisch ist **viel** besser als meines.

67.

Re-write the sentences in the way suggested below:

Example: Tom is not so stupid as <u>Bill</u>
        <u>Bill</u> is more stupid than Tom.

a) Mr Brown's house is not so big as Mr Baker's.

....

b) My brother is not so old as my uncle.

....

c) A bike is not so expensive as a motorbike.

....

d) A banana is not so cheap as an apple.

....

e) A cat is not so heavy as a cow.

....

f) Other aeroplanes are not so fast as Concorde.

....

g) Jenny is not so proud as her sister.

....

h) A cigarette is not so strong as a cigar.

....

i) A donkey is not so beautiful as a horse.

....

k) Ian is not so short as his brother.

....

l) Mr Brown's German is not so good as Herr Huber's.

....

68.

Translate into English;

a) Unsere neue Küche ist größer als die alte.

b) England ist größer als Wales.

c) London ist bedeutender als Cardiff.

d) Toms Freundin ist viel jünger, als sie aussieht.

e) Tom ist größer als seine Freundin.

f) Er ist aber nicht so groß wie sein Vater.

g) Janes Schuhe sind modischer als meine.

h) Der Film war viel interessanter als das Buch.

i) Deutsch ist viel schwerer als Englisch.

k) Dies ist der spannendste Film, den ich je gesehen habe.

l) Diese Übung war nicht ganz so leicht wie die andere.

69.
Translate into German:

a) The less you say, the better.

....

b) The more careful you are, the better.

....

c) The road became narrower and narrower.

....

d) The girls grew more and more excited.

....

e) London is much larger than Dover.

....

f) The situation became more and more serious.

....

g) These apples taste worse than the others.

....

h) This book is less boring than the last one I read.

....

i) My essay got worse and worse towards the end.

....

k) Jimmy made more and more mistakes.

....

l) Our new car is less expensive than the last one.

....

70.

**Hier hat der Fehlerteufel zugeschlagen!
Verbessere bitte alle Fehler aus Schülerarbeiten:**

a) John is older as his cousin.

....

b) John is not so clever than Jim.

....

c) Barbara is intelligenter than her sister.

....

d) Tom's German is bader than his neighbour's.

....

e) Tom hasn't got much friends.

....

f) The book cost fewer money than we had expected.

....

g) The nearest train to Manchester leaves in 30 minutes.

....

h) St. Paul's Cathedral is one of the most well-known sights of London.

....

71.
Comprehension Test: The American And His Car

The car is the key to American life and amusement.
Going for a walk, whether in the town or in the country, is just not part of the American way of life. An English journalist strolling along the road in Los Angeles was questioned by the police because it seemed so strange to them to see somebody walking. Except in town centers it is rare to find a sidewalk beside the road. A person who tries to go about on foot at night may find that there are no street lights and that he will be attacked by angry dogs from the houses which he passes. The dogs so seldom see anybody walking that, like the Los Angeles police, they think he must be a burglar.

I. Answer in complete sentences:

a) Do Americans like to go for long walks? Say why or why not.

....

b) What happened to an English journalist in Los Angeles?

....

c) Where can you find sidewalks in the U.S.A.?

....

d) What can happen to someone who goes for a walk at night? (Two ideas)

....

....

e) Why are some dogs so angry? (Two ideas)

....

....

II. Fill in the correct forms of the adjectives:

a) Only .... (few) Americans go about on foot.

b) Los Angeles has .... (few) inhabitants .... New York.

c) Americans spend .... (little) money on sidewalks .... Europeans.

d) There are .... (many) sidewalks in Munich .... in Los Angeles.

e) Los Angeles is one of the .... (beautiful) cities in California.

f) American cars are usually not .... (quick) .... European

cars, but they are .... (comfortable).

g) The journalist saw a dog which was .... (angry) .... all the dogs
he had ever seen before.

III. Translate into English:

a) Der Bericht über die amerikanische Lebensart ist höchst interessant.

....

b) Kalifornien ist heute bedeutender als viele andere Staaten.

....

c) In Kalifornien ist es sonniger und wärmer als in anderen Teilen der USA.

....

d) In den USA ist es ungewöhnlicher, zu Fuß zu gehen, als in England.

....

Kapitel 7
Adverb (Adverb, Umstandswort)

72.
Lernhilfen für die Übungen.

A) Formen:

beautiful	beautifully	Adjektiv + **-ly** = **Adverb**
nice	nicely	'e' bleibt vor -ly, außer bei: due/duly; true/truly; whole/wholly

Beachte:			
angry	angrily	y	→ ily (aber: shyly)
horrible	horribly	ible	→ ibly
fashionable	fashionably	able	→ ably
economic	economically	ic	→ ically (aber: publicly)
friendly	in a friendly **way**		

Bill is a **fast** runner.	Adjektiv + Adverb haben dieselbe Form!
He runs **fast**.	auch: early, daily, long

Mr Brown works **hard**. (= schwer)	Das Adverb hat **2 Formen** und **2 Bedeutungen**!
He **hardly** forgets things. (= kaum)	auch: late (spät), lately (in letzter Zeit); pretty (ziemlich), prettily (hübsch); fair (fair), fairly (ziemlich)

B) Steigerung:

soon	sooner	soonest	auch: high, fast, early!
carefully	more carefully	most carefully	2- und mehrsilbige Adverbien!
well	better	best	andere Formen: auch: badly, worse, worst; much, more, most; a little, less, least!

C) Unterschied zwischen Adjektiv und Adverb:

They met a **polite** lady. She is always **polite**.	Das **Adjektiv** beschreibt ein **Substantiv** (lady) **oder Pronomen** (She)!
The lady behaved **politely**.	Das **Adverb** bestimmt ein **Verb** (behaved),
She was **very** polite.	ein **Adjektiv** (polite).
She behaved **extremely** politely.	ein anderes **Adverb** (politely)
Unfortunately, there was no member of the station staff present.	oder einen **ganzen Satz!**
aber: They looked **disinterested**. She found it **rude**.	**Kein Adverb** nach gewissen Verben! → **82**

D) Wortstellung:

The boy behaved **badly**. The lady speaks German **fluently**.	**Adverb of Manner** (Adverb der Art und Weise) nach dem Verb bzw. Objekt!
The boy was **extremely** rude. He behaved **very** rudely. They **simply** concentrated on their newspapers. The boy could **hardly** speak.	**Adverb of Degree** (Gradadverb) **vor** dem Adjektiv (rude) oder Adverb (rudely) oder Verb (concentrated; speak)! → **84**
The lady **often** goes by train. I have **never** seen her before.	**Adverb of Frequency** (Häufigkeitsadverb) **vor dem Verb** (goes, seen)! auch: always, usually, rarely → **84**

73.
Text: On A Station Platform

It was late evening and a crowd of young people were hanging about, behaving badly and frightening the travellers who were waiting for the train. Unfortunately, no member of the station staff was present and most people tried to look disinterested, reading newspapers and pretending not to notice the noisy group.

But one old lady spoke up. "Would you kindly stop swearing," she asked one of the loudest youths. "I find it rude."

He stopped and looked at her open-mouthed. The other travellers simply concentrated on their newspapers. "Rude, am I?" the youth replied aggressively, while his grinning friends waited to see what he would do. "I'll show you how rude I can be, lady!" – and he stripped off his trousers.

Quietly the old lady picked up the trousers with the handle of her umbrella and dropped them on to the railway lines, where they fell between the rails.

to behave	=	sich benehmen
to frighten	=	erschrecken
disinterested	=	unbeteiligt
to pretend	=	vortäuschen, so tun als ob

74.
Fill in proper words from the text:

a) A crowd of young people were behaving ....

b) ...., no railwayman was on the platform.

c) Most travellers looked ....

d) The old lady asked the youth if he would .... stop swearing.

e) The other people .... concentrated on their newspapers.

f) The youth reacted .... to the old lady's words.

g) He looked at her ....

h) .... the old lady picked up his trousers.

75.
Translate into English:

a) Die Gruppe junger Leute benahm sich wirklich schlecht.

....

b) Die meisten Reisenden schienen die lärmenden jungen Leute nicht zu bemerken.

....

c) Viele von ihnen schauten unbeteiligt drein.

....

d) Sie konzentrierten sich ganz einfach auf ihre Zeitungen.

....

e) Der lauteste Jugendliche benahm sich ungehobelter als seine Freunde.

....

76.
Adjective and Adverb:

a) One of the boys had .... manners. He behaved .... (bad)

b) His manners weren't .... He didn't behave .... (good)

c) The old lady was .... She spoke to the boy .... (angry)

d) Normally she is very .... She speaks .... (friendly)

e) The group were .... They moved about .... (noisy)

f) One of them seemed to be .... He was jumping about .... (mad).

g) Most other people were .... They looked into their papers ....
   (quiet).

h) The youth talked .... nonsense. His behaviour was ....
   wrong (complete).

i) One gentleman was very .... He .... ran to another
   platform. (anxious)

k) The youth's behaviour was .... It was .... rude.
   (extreme)

l) The lady was very .... She looked .... in her red coat.
   (nice)

77.

Adjective or adverb?

a) The .... (friendly) old lady found the youth's behaviour

.... (impolite).

b) Most of the passengers looked .... (tired).

c) The tea at the station buffet smells .... (good) and the

sandwiches taste .... (excellent).

d) A gentleman said to the buffet girl, "I want my tea ...." (sweet).

e) A boy ran on to the platform .... (excited).

f) The hairdresser had cut his hair .... (short).

g) An old man sat down .... (slow); he was ....

.... (serious + ill).

h) The youth's plan went .... (wrong); he was ....

.... (complete + quiet).

i) There are .... doors in the trains; doors open and close

.... (automatic).

k) Most people travel to town .... (daily).

l) The train was one minute .... (early).

m) The passengers didn't have to wait .... (long).

78.

Where must you put the adverb?

a) The incident happened.

+ on a platform in London
+ last night

....

b) A crowd of young people were behaving . . . + **very** + **rudely**

....

c) An old lady went to the loudest youth. + **slowly**

....

d) She found his behaviour bad. + **terribly**

....

e) The other travellers read their papers
and pretended to see nothing. + **quietly**

....

f) They concentrated on their papers. + **simply**

....

g) It was surprising that they said nothing. + **really**

....

h) The old lady's reaction was right. + **absolutely**

....

i) The stationmaster was not present. + **unfortunately**

....

k) He could have told the youths to behave . . . + **more politely**

....

l) The lady dropped the trousers on to the
railway lines. + **simply**

....

m) The boy didn't jump between the rails. + **luckily**

....

90

79.

Translate into English:

a) Das junge Mädchen sah in seinem neuen Kleid sehr schön aus.

....

b) Der Bahnhofsvorsteher sah in seiner Uniform sehr schick aus.

....

c) Ein alter Mann sah ärgerlich aus. Er schaute den Jugendlichen ärgerlich an.

....

....

d) Es ist wirklich erstaunlich, daß die alte Dame so schnell reagierte.

....

....

e) Leider haben heute nur wenige Leute so viel Mut.

....

f) Ein kleines Mädchen lief schnell zu seiner Mutter.

....

g) Der unhöfliche Jugendliche sprach aufgeregt mit seinen Kameraden.

....

....

h) Er benahm sich immer unhöflicher.

....

i) Je strenger die alte Dame sprach, desto nervöser reagierte der junge Mann.

....

....

80.

Übersetzungstraining:

Example: I <u>happened to</u> meet the old lady. (Englisch: Verb!)

    = Ich traf die alte Dame <u>zufällig</u>. (Deutsch: Adverb!)

Verwende folgende Adverbien: **angeblich – anscheinend – gern – hoffentlich – lieber – sicher – vermutlich – weiter.**

a) I hope my son will behave more politely.

....

b) Most travellers went on reading their papers.

....

c) I suppose the boys have gone home.

....

d) I'm sure I'll meet the old lady again.

....

e) I'm fond of travelling by train.

....

f) My grandmother prefers going by motorbike.

....

g) Mrs Brown is said to be an excellent cook.

....

h) Mr Brown seems to be ill.

....

81.

Hier war wieder der Fehlerteufel am Werk!
Verbessere die Fehler aus Schüler-arbeiten:

a) Susi ist schön.
   Susy is beautifully.

....

b) Sie sieht schön aus.
   She looks beautifully.

....

c) Sie kleidet sich immer schön.
   She always dresses beautiful.

....

d) Unsere Schulaufgabe war äußerst schwierig.
   Our test was extreme difficult.

....

e) Mein Freund Billy arbeitet wirklich tüchtig.
   My friend Billy works real hardly.

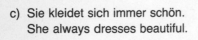

....

f) Das neue Auto fährt sehr schnell.
   The new car goes very fastly.

....

g) Hans spricht sehr gut Englisch.
   Hans speaks English very good.

....

82.
Paukliste: Verben mit prädikativem Adjektiv.
Example: They **looked** disinterested.

to be	sein
to become	werden
to get	werden
to grow	werden
to seem	scheinen
to look	ausschauen
to feel	sich fühlen
to remain	bleiben
to taste	schmecken
to smell	riechen nach
to sound	klingen
to consider	halten für
to remain	bleiben
to stand	stehen
to sit	sitzen
to arrive	ankommen
to return	zurückkehren

Entscheidend ist, daß etwas über ein Substantiv oder Pronomen ausgesagt wird und nicht eine Tätigkeit (= Verb!) näher bestimmt wird!

Tom remained calm.	Tom blieb ruhig.
They returned happy.	Sie kehrten glücklich zurück.
It sounds good.	Es klingt gut.
I consider it wrong.	Ich halte es für falsch.

83.
Häufigkeitsadverbien (Adverbs of frequency)
Example: The lady **often** goes by train.

always	immer
hardly ever	kaum jemals
frequently	häufig
never	niemals
occasionally	gelegentlich
often	oft
rarely	selten
seldom	selten
sometimes	manchmal

84.
Gradadverbien (Adverbs of degree)
Example: The boy was **extremely** rude.

very	sehr
quite	ganz, völlig
really	wirklich
exceptionally	außerordentlich
extremely	äußerst
particularly	besonders

85.
Comprehension Test: On A Station Platform (2)

There was complete silence, broken only by a train pulling in, right over the trousers.

"What am I going to do?" cried the youth. His friends began to laugh and quickly pushed their way on to the train.

The boy hesitated for a second but, as he didn't want to miss the last train home, he decided to leave his trousers lying between the rails and jumped in.

As the old lady stepped in after him, she said to her opponent: "Let that be a lesson to you. You'll have to ask the stationmaster for help."

No one spoke to her on the train, neither the grinning gang, nor the other travellers, probably because they felt uneasy. Most of the passengers admired her and thought how marvellous it would be if everybody had the courage to stand up against such bad behaviour.

I. Answer in complete sentences:

a) What was the silence broken by?

....

b) What did the boy's friends do?

....

c) Why did the boy get on the train?

....

d) Why did no one speak to the old lady?

....

e) What did most of the travellers think of her?

....

II. Decide between adverb and adjective:

a) Most of the travellers felt (uneasy, uneasily) ....

b) The situation seemed (serious, seriously) ....

c) The idea of the lady sounds (good, well) ....

d) She found the boy's behaviour (awful, awfully) ....

e) Some people on the platform were (tired, tiredly) ....

f) They didn't get (angry, angrily) ....

g) The boys were growing (bored, boredly) .... with their friend.

h) Suddenly everybody was (complete, completely) .... silent for a moment.

i) There was (complete, completely) .... silence for a short time.

III. Translate into German:

a) They quickly pushed their way on to the train.

....

b) Neither the grinning gang, nor the other travellers spoke to the lady.

....

c) Probably they felt uneasy.

....

d) Most of the passengers admired the old lady.

....

Kapitel 8
Relativpronomen (Relative Pronouns)

86.

Lernhilfen für die Übungen.

A) Defining Relative Clauses (Notwendige Relativsätze)

Subject (Wer oder Was?)

The man	**who** **that**	was here yesterday has gone to London.
The key	**which** **that**	is lying in the grass is mine.

Diese Relativsätze **definieren** das **Subjekt** (man, key) genauer: Sie sind wichtig!

Object (Wen oder Was?)

The man	**whom** **that** —*	you met yesterday has gone to London.
The key	**which** **that** —*	I put on the table is mine.

Wenn das Relativpronomen **Objekt** ist, wird es in der Regel* **weggelassen**! Man spricht von **contact clauses**.

Preposition

The man **to whom** you spoke has gone to London.

formal English!

The man	**who** **whom** **that** —*	you spoke	**to**	has gone to London.

informal English!
 Präposition am Ende!

They key **at which** you were looking is mine.

formal English!

The key	**that** **which** —*	you were looking	**at**	is mine.

informal English!

B) Non-defining Relative Clauses (Entbehrliche Relativsätze)

Mr Brown, **who** lives in London, is a friendly man.	Beachte: Diese Relativsätze
Mr Brown, **whose** wife you met, is a friendly man.	bieten zusätzliche Informationen. Sie
Mr Brown, **whom** you met yesterday, is a friendly man.	wären aber ent- behrlich!
Mr Brown, **to whom** I was speaking, is a friendly man. ↑ Person!	**whom** ist erforder- lich!

Chess, **which** is an old game, isn't easy to play. ↑ Sache!	**which** für Sachen!

I have been waiting for Tom the whole morning, **and** it was very boring. I have been waiting for Tom the whole morning, **which** was very boring.	**which** kann sich auf einen ganzen Satz beziehen!
Mr Green gave the key to his wife, **and** she passed it to Tom. Mr Green gave the key to his wife, **who** passed it to Tom.	**who** anstelle von 'and'! Man spricht von **Connective Clauses!**

Fehlerquelle:

a) Keine Präposition **vor** 'that'!
   The key **that** you were looking **at** . . .
b) Kein 'that' anstelle von **whom** im entbehrlichen Relativsatz!
c) **that, which bzw. who** dürfen in notwendigen Relativsätzen nur wegfallen, wenn sie **nicht Subjekt** sind!
d) Für **that which** und **all that** verwendet man **what**!
   I gave them **what** they wanted.

87.
Text: What Bad Luck!

At times it's a pity not to be a competent burglar.
Of course, I don't like those fellows who take other people's property, but I must admire the skill with which some of them are able to open any door they choose with a piece of bent wire. There have been many occasions when I would have given anything to have had a little knowledge of their job.
Last Tuesday morning, I found the door of my toolshed locked, and the key, which I keep in a hole in a tree beside the shed, had been taken away during the night. It must now be lying under the mass of cut branches which the gardener had left beside the door of the shed. What bad luck! In addition to this misfortune it started to rain. I stood for some time and attacked the key-hole with all four of my screwdrivers which I have used to open the door with, whenever the key has disappeared, but always with the same negative result.
Next I bent a piece of wire, pushed it in, twisted it around and – nothing happened.

property	=	Besitz, Eigentum
to admire	=	bewundern
a piece of wire	=	ein Stück Draht
toolshed	=	Geräteschuppen
to lock	=	zusperren
misfortune	=	Mißgeschick

88.

Answer in complete sentences:

a) Why does the writer not like burglars?

....

b) Why does he wish he was like them?

....

c) Which doors can the burglars open?

....

d) Where does the man usually keep the key of his toolshed?

....

e) What had happened to the key last Monday night?

....

f) Who had left the cut branches beside the door of the shed?

....

89.

Translate into English:

a) Der Einbrecher, der alle Türen öffnen konnte, war nicht mein Freund.

....

b) Einige Einbrecher können jede Tür, die sie auswählen, mit einem Stück Draht öffnen.

....

c) Ich fand den Schuppen, den ich gekauft hatte, verschlossen.

....

d) Der Schlüssel, den ich nicht finden konnte, war verschwunden.

....

90.
Make sentences like the first sentence:

Example: The lady who played the piano is a teacher from my school.

a) The policeman / catch / the burglar / great runner

......

b) The lady / cook / the pizza / Italian exchange teacher

......

c) The person / write / the letter / my girlfriend

......

Example: Mr Brown, whom you met yesterday, is a friendly man.

d) Mrs Cook / meet / last week / housewife

......

e) Miss Type / speak to / two days ago / secretary

......

f) The teacher / see / last night / my form master

......

Example: The key they put on the table is mine.

g) The girl / speak to / my girlfriend

......

h) The secretary / interview / very competent

......

i) The film / see / very thrilling

......

k) The book / read / extremely boring

......

91.

Fill in 'who', 'which', 'whom', or nothing:

a) I was looking for the key, ... had been taken away.

b) I admire burglars .... can open a door.

c) There was no tool .... I could open the door with.

d) What would the writer, ... was no burglar, like to be at times?

e) His friend, ... he could not ask, would have been able to open the door.

f) A hut .... is made of wood can be called a shed.

g) My friend, ... isn't a burglar, can open any door.

h) The man .... I had bought the shed from told me to repair it.

i) Everyone .... has got the right key can open a door.

k) The shed, ... is my property, is rather large.

l) The piece of bent wire .... I found was of no use.

m) What can people do .... want to sell their house?

n) The gardener, ... I've never seen before, had left the cut branches beside the shed.

92.

Link the following sentences and leave out the relative pronoun where possible:

a) The garden is rather large. I own it now.

....

b) The man lives in Bradford. I got to know him.

....

c) The shed was locked. It is my property.

....

d) The key was lost. I have been looking for it.

....

e) The burglar is not my friend. You have seen him.

....

f) I met the old gardener. My friend likes him very much.

....

g) I bought the shed from Mr Traynor. You will meet him next week.

....

h) This house is the finest in town. Mr Traynor lives in it.

....

i) That lady is my new neighbour. You saw her yesterday.

....

k) Last week I went to my shed. It is in a bad state.

....

l) Mr Traynor is a nice man. You will like him.

....

93.

Cross the right answers:

a) The screwdriver ☐ whose he needs   is too small.
                           ☐ which he needs
                           ☐ needs

b) The burglar ☐ about who we spoke   opened the door.
              ☐ about whom we spoke of
              ☐ we spoke about

c) The key ☐ that I was looking   lay under the leaves.
         ☐ I was looking for
         ☐ for what I was looking

d) The girls ☐ which you met   will come to our party.
           ☐ that you met them
           ☐ that you met

e) The girl ☐ whose bike was stolen   is my sister.
         ☐ bike was stolen
         ☐ whom bike was stolen

f) The boy ☐ lost the money   is waiting outside.
        ☐ who lost the money
        ☐ he lost the money

g) The boy ☐ whom book you borrowed   needs it tomorrow.
        ☐ which book you borrowed
        ☐ whose book you borrowed

h) I enjoyed the film ☐ what we saw last night.
                  ☐ which we saw it last night.
                  ☐ we saw last night.

94.

Der Fehlerteufel war wieder am Werk! Verbessere die Fehler aus Schülerarbeiten.

a) Mrs Smith, which is Angela's mother, is a nice woman.

....

....

b) His car, who is standing outside, can do 120 miles an hour.

....

....

c) That's the bus for it I've been waiting for three hours.

....

d) Mr Parson, who I was speaking, is a teacher.

....

e) Tom, whose is Susy's boyfriend, is one of the best pupils in class.

....

f) The church at which you are looking at is a wonderful building.

....

g) The dance what you saw last night was a folk dance.

....

h) Susy Brown who is my girlfriend we met at the party.

....

95.
Comprehension Test: What Bad Luck! (2)

I began to look for the key in the branches into which it must have fallen. Then I remembered that when I was a young boy, I usually prayed to St Anthony, whom I begged for the return of anything I had lost.

I tried praying now, but obviously the Saint did not like my thoughts of breaking down the door, smashing the window, or selling the house. Whatever I was thinking of, the Saint did not help and I couldn't solve the problem of this door which could not be opened.

It was raining more heavily than ever when I found the key, which was only a rusty little thing, under the leaves.

I opened the door of the shed, left it open and put the key in a new secret place where I thought it was safe.

I have been looking for it ever since.

I. Answer the following questions in a complete sentence:

a) Why did the man look for the key in the branches?

....

b) What did he usually beg from St Anthony?

....

c) Why couldn't he solve the problem of that door?

....

d) What was the key like that was hiding under the leaves?

....

e) What did he think of the new secret place for the key?

....

II. Make one sentence using relative clauses:

a) The shed stands in a beautiful garden. I keep my tools in it.

....

b) When I was looking for the key I finally remembered St Anthony. He usually helped me to find lost things.

....

....

c) St Anthony is a Saint. I used to pray to him when I was a boy.

....

d) The Saint did not answer my prayer. I could have used his help.

....

e) Have you met the gardener? He helps me mowing the lawn. The lawn is especially green.

....

....

f) The gardener is an old man. He lives in a little village nearby.

....

g) In my garden there are three fruit-trees. Neither of the tree had any fruit this summer.

....

....

h) Last autumn I felled two trees. One of them was extremely high.

....

III. Translate into English:

a) Mein Onkel, der in Edinburgh wohnt, hat einen schönen Garten.

b) Der Garten liegt an einem Wald, der nicht weit vom Fluß ist.

c) Es ist dieser kleine Fluß, von dem ich dir erzählt habe.

d) Der Fluß, dessen Ufer sehr steil sind, ist sehr sauber.

e) Letzten Sommer besuchte M. Blanc, dessen Kinder immer im Fluß schwimmen, meinen Onkel.

f) M. Blanc ist der Freund, mit dem du einmal gesprochen hast.

g) Die Kinder fanden den Schlüssel, nach dem mein Onkel so lange Zeit gesucht hatte.

h) Die Hütte, auf deren Dach die Kinder herumkletterten, mußte repariert werden.

i) Es ist dieselbe Hütte, in der mein Onkel im Sommer wohnt.

k) Auch im Winter dort zu leben, ist ein Problem, worüber mein Onkel immer nachdenkt.

Kapitel 9

Oneself – Each Other

96.
Lernhilfen für die Übungen.

Marianne bought **herself** a hat.
   (= kaufte **sich**)
The old man talked **to himself.**
   (= sprach mit **sich selbst**)

Du verwendest das **Reflexivpronomen** (Formen von 'oneself'), wenn Subjekt und Objekt die **gleiche** Person bezeichnen!

Marianne bought her sister a hat.
Marianne bought **her** a hat.

Marianne closed the door **behind her.**

Beachte:
Andere Person (her sister)!
Personalpronomen meist nach Präposition mit örtlicher Bedeutung!

Marianne **remembers**   Peter.
Marianne **erinnert sich an**   Peter.

Marianne **is glad.**
Marianne **freut sich.**

Im Englischen werden viele Verben **nicht reflexiv** gebraucht!
→ Paukliste **105**

Marianne herself saw Prince Charles.
   (= **selbst**)
She did all the housework **herself.**

Mit 'oneself' kannst du ein Substantiv **hervorheben**!

Marianne and Bob looked at **each other.**
(sich, einander)

Du verwendest **each other** bzw. **one another**, wenn eine wechselseitige Beziehung vorliegt!

Vergleiche:
Marianne and Bob saw **themselves** in the mirror. (= sich selber)

Marianne and Bob **met** twice a week.
(trafen sich)

Oft ist **each other** nicht notwendig!
→ **105**

97.
Text: Au-Pair Girls

Thirty thousand au-pair girls come to Britain every year. They offer their help, and in exchange they hope to get a chance to improve their English and to get to know the English way of life.

The relationship between the housewife and her au-pair is whatever they make it. Some girls have to work all day long – a few even say that they are treated like slaves! Most of them, however, have plenty of free time, which they can use as they like.

Marianne, for example, an 18-year-old German girl, works six hours a day, helping in the household, collecting the children from school and looking after them when their parents are away. She sleeps in the family's guestroom, with an extra bed for girlfriends to stay overnight. Marianne feels quite happy now, but the job she had before was a very bad experience: "My host family rarely talked to me," she remembered, "and they wouldn't let me have friends in. I was very lonely."

to improve   = verbessern
relationship = Beziehung, Verhältnis
to treat   = behandeln
slave   = Sklave

98.
Mark the correct translation (Look at the text):

a) Marianne fühlt sich ganz wohl.
   ☐ Marianne feels her quite happy.
   ☐ Marianne feels herself quite happy.
   ☐ Marianne feels quite happy.

b) Sie erinnert sich an eine andere Familie.
   ☐ She remembers her another family.
   ☐ She remembers herself another family.
   ☐ She remembers another family.

c) Die Gastgeber sprachen selten zu mir.
   ☐ The hosts rarely talked to me.
   ☐ The hosts rarely talked to herself.
   ☐ The hosts rarely talked.

99.
Add the correct form of "oneself":

a) Most housewives don't want to do all the work ....

b) Marianne introduced .... to her host family.

c) Marianne and her friend enjoyed .... at some parties.

d) Marianne, you must look after ....

e) One day Marianne cut .... in the finger.

f) The children washed .... as quickly as they could.

g) They hurt .... badly when roller skating.

h) Marianne read "Help ...." at the counter of the self-service restaurant.

100.
Fill in the reflexive pronoun, if necessary:

a) Marianne joined .... a group of young people.

b) At the first meeting she introduced .... to all the boys and girls.

c) The group meets .... every Saturday night.

d) They enjoy .... with films or dancing.

e) Marianne wondered .... how she could have stayed a month with her first family.

f) She couldn't remember .... having met .... such nice people before.

g) Marianne and two other girls did all the preparations for a barbecue party

....

h) When she cut the meat, Marianne hurt .... with the knife.

i) The guests helped .... to some more food.

101.
Complete:

a) Marianne and Bob met .... in front of the disco.

b) There was a lot of fog. They couldn't see ....

c) Marianne and Bob get along with .... very well.

d) They want to become engaged .... soon.

e) They understand .... excellently.

102.

Translate into English:

a) Marianne und John sahen sich im Spiegel an, ehe sie auf die Party gingen.

b) Marianne und John blickten sich überrascht an, als sie sich zufällig trafen.

c) Marianne hat sich in letzter Zeit sehr verändert.

d) Marianne spricht mit Mr Brown; sie spricht oft mit ihm.

e) Mrs Brown spricht oft mit sich selbst.

f) Marianne wird sich immer an die erste Familie erinnern.

g) Erinnerst du dich an deinen Besuch in London?

h) Marianne verrichtet die Hausarbeit ganz alleine.

i) Ihr Freund ist sehr praktisch. Er repariert sein Auto selber.

103.

Hier hat der Fehlerteufel zugeschlagen!
Verbessere die Fehler aus Schülerarbeiten:

a) I cut me with a knife the other day.

....

b) The girls enjoyed oneself very much.

....

c) You must all look after yourself, girls.

....

d) Peter hurt him when he fell off the tree.

....

e) Do you remember yourself on my birthday party?

....

f) The weather hasn't changed itself.

....

g) I wonder oneself why Tom hasn't come.

....

h) Have we got to do the work all by ourself?

....

i) Sandra closed the gate behind herself.

....

104.
Comprehension Test: Au-Pair Girls (2)

How do you find a place as an au-pair?
The best way is either through personal recommendation or by enquiring at a British Consulate. Knowing that difficulties may arise, the British government has expressed the hope that an au-pair girl will be treated like a 'daughter of the house'. The golden rule is not to ask her to do anything one wouldn't do oneself.
In general, an au-pair should be given a room to herself, one and a half free days a week and enough pocket money. As a rule she will have most of her meals with the family, and there should be time for her to attend English language classes, go out in the evening, and enjoy herself with her friends.

I. Answer in complete sentences:

a) How should au-pair girls be treated?

....

b) What is the golden rule for an au-pair girl?

....

c) How much spare time should a girl have?

....

d) Where should she eat?

....

e) What does the text say about English language classes?

....

f) Which free time activities are mentioned?

....

II. Mark the wrong (!) words in each of the following sentences with a cross:

a) Marianne and her first host family didn't get on well
   with ☐ herself
        ☐ themselves.
        ☐ each other.

b) Marianne had not imagined ☐ herself   that the job would be so hard.
                              ☐ oneself
                              ☐ each other

c) Her first family proved ☐ herself   to be rather unfriendly.
                           ☐ themselves
                           ☐ itself

d) Her second host family, however, took ☐ her   to a lot of parties where
                                         ☐ herself
                                         ☐ each other

   they all enjoyed ☐ each other.
                    ☐ themselves.
                    ☐ herself.

e) One day Marianne ☐ met   an old gentleman who always
                    ☐ met her
                    ☐ met herself

   talked to ☐ himself.
             ☐ him.
             ☐ each other.

f) When she saw him again, he said 'Hello' and they started to talk to
   ☐ each other
   ☐ themselves.
   ☐ himself.

117

III. Translate into English:

a) Liebe Peggy.
   Du schriebst, daß du dich für ein Au-pair-Mädchen interessieren würdest.

   ....

   ....

b) Wir haben beschlossen, eines zu nehmen.

   ....

c) Als wir uns am Flugplatz trafen und uns anschauten, bemerkten wir, daß wir
   uns schon kannten.

   ....

   ....

d) Hanni, wie sich das Mädchen nennt, konnte sich auch an unsere Begegnung
   erinnern.

   ....

e) Wir fragen uns, ob Hanni ein ganzes Jahr bei uns bleiben wird.

   ....

f) Hanni kümmert sich um die Kinder.

   ....

g) Sie hat sich unserem Jugendclub angeschlossen.

   ....

h) Wir helfen uns, die andere Sprache zu lernen.

   ....

i) Ich muß mich entschuldigen, aber ich darf mich heute nicht verspäten.

   ....

k) Alles Gute! Diana

   ....

105.
Paukliste wichtiger Vokabeln:

<u>Example:</u> Marianne **remembers** Peter (= **erinnert sich an**)

to approach	sich nähern
to apologise	sich entschuldigen
to change	sich ändern
to differ from	sich unterscheiden von
to feel	sich fühlen
to happen	sich ereignen
to imagine	sich einbilden
to join	sich anschließen an
to lie down	sich hinlegen
to move	sich bewegen
to prove	sich erweisen als
to refuse	sich weigern
to remember	sich erinnern an
to sell well	sich gut verkaufen
to sit down	sich setzen
to wonder	sich fragen

<u>Example:</u> Marianne **is glad**. (= **freut sich**)

I'm afraid	ich fürchte mich
I'm angry	ich ärgere mich
I'm ashamed	ich schäme mich
I catch a cold	ich erkälte mich
I'm glad	ich freue mich
I'm interested in	ich interessiere mich für
I'm late	ich verspäte mich
I lose my way	ich verirre mich
I make up my mind	ich entscheide mich

<u>Example:</u> Marianne and Bob **met** twice a week. (= **trafen sich**)

to meet	sich treffen
to part	sich trennen
to quarrel	sich streiten

Kapitel 10

Some / Any   Each / Every

106.
Lernhilfen für die Übungen.

A) Verwendung von 'some' and 'any':

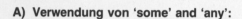

Mr Brown drank **some** coffee.
↑
    Bejahte Aussage!

He did **not** drink **any** tea.
 ↑ ↑
 Negative Aussage!

Can I have **some** more coffee? (Yes.)
 ↑
  Frage, bei der eine **bejahende Antwort sicher** ist! (Der Kaffee steht da!)

Have you got **any** toast at home?
   ↑
   Frage, bei der Ja oder Nein als Antwort möglich ist!

Would you like **some** coffee?
 ↑
  Höfliches Angebot!

If you have **any** problems, ask me.
↑ ↑
Es herrschen **Unsicherheit oder Zweifel!**

You can take **any** cup you like.
  ↑

   any im bejahenden Satz: jede (beliebige); ganz gleich, welche

B) Formen von 'some' und 'any':

some	any	not ... any	= no
somebody	anybody	not ... anybody	= nobody
someone	anyone	not ... anyone	= no-one
something	anything	not ... anything	= nothing
somewhere	anywhere	not ... anywhere	= nowhere

C) Verwendung von 'each' und 'every':

Every boy likes football.
↑
Jeder (ohne Ausnahme)!

Tom and Ian bought a book. **Each** boy paid for the book.
↑
Jeder (einzelne)!

There are 25 boys in our class. **Each of** them plays football.
↑
Jeder von ihnen (aus einer bestimmten Zahl)!

D) Übersetzungstraining:

Mr Brown goes to a concert every week.	Herr Brown geht jede Woche ins Konzert.
Everybody listened to the music.	Jeder hörte der Musik zu.
They did everything to help us.	Sie taten alles, um uns zu helfen.
I can't find the key, although I've looked everywhere.	Ich kann den Schlüssel nicht finden, obwohl ich überall geschaut habe.

107.
Text: The Driving Test

With a silent prayer, Angela did as she had been taught: she put the car in first gear, checked the mirror, looked over her right shoulder, signalled that she was about to move off, released the handbrake and stepped on the accelerator. Nothing happened. Knowing how nervous driving-test candidates feel, the examiner suggested gently: "Now take your time, nobody is perfect at the beginning. Let's start all over again."

Blushing, Angela started the engine this time, and sailed through her test without any further mistakes.

Situations like that may occur everywhere, and taking a driving test has always been an exciting experience.

In 1979, more than a million and a half learners took the test in Great Britain – more than half of them failed.

Of course, there are many driving schools in Britain, but nobody is obliged to take driving lessons there. You can acquire all your skills in any car you like and can be taught by any of your friends or relatives.

prayer	=	Gebet
gear	=	Gang (beim Auto!)
to release	=	lösen
handbrake	=	Handbremse
accelerator	=	Gaspedal
to suggest	=	vorschlagen
experience	=	Erlebnis
to acquire	=	erwerben, erlangen

108.

Answer in complete sentences:

a) What happened after the lady had stepped on the accelerator?

....

b) Did the examiner say that everybody must be perfect?

....

c) Is it necessary that everyone in Britain takes driving lessons?

....

d) In what sort of car can you acquire your skill?

....

109.

Make questions to the following answers:

a) ....

Yes, I've met him somewhere before.

b) ....

Yes, she has found something for her nervousness.

c) ....

Yes, she talked to somebody about her test.

d) ....

Yes, she managed to pass some parts of the test.

e) ....

No, she didn't make any mistakes.

f) ....

Yes, of course, you can take some more lessons.

110.

Make the following sentences negative (2 Möglichkeiten pro Satz!):
Example: There isn't anybody waiting. There's nobody waiting.

a) There are some driving schools around here.

....

....

b) This school has got some motorbikes.

....

....

c) The examiner asked some further questions.

....

....

d) The candidate knew something about traffic signs.

....

....

e) He had seen the test paper somewhere before.

....

....

f) After the first group the examiner asked someone else.

....

....

111.

'each' or 'every':

a) .... time she tried to start the car, it didn't run.

b) In this driving school there are tests .... month.

c) .... of the candidates had taken lessons before.

d) The lessons are £ 7 ....

e) Fifty persons out of .... hundred failed the test.

f) In .... case, the examiner had to take over the braking or steering.

g) .... other day my friend practised driving.

h) The candidate and the examiner didn't like .... other.

i) .... one in our family has got a car.

k) .... of us is fond of big cars.

l) You will find driving schools .... where in the country.

m) It's impossible for a candidate to know .... thing.

n) .... of the questions in a test must be answered.

o) .... one who wants to pass a test, must be well-prepared.

p) My friend has a driving lesson .... other day.

q) His sister only takes a lesson .... now and then.

112.
Comprehension Test: The Driving Test (2)

Before starting out, however, a learner driver must get a provisional licence. This gives him the right to drive on any British road, except motorways, as long as he is accompanied by someone who holds a full British licence. He also has to put L-plates ("L" for "learner") on the front and rear of the car.

Statistics say that too many learners take the test without enough practice. You can even take your test in any car you like. You can also use your own one. If you want to do so, check it carefully. Otherwise you might not get your driving-licence, for the reason that your car might break down. This was the case when a well-prepared candidate set off on the test-drive somewhere in the country. After a few miles the engine suddenly stopped and something was broken. The examiner and the candidate had to walk home together.

I. Questions on the text:

a) Where is a learner driver allowed to drive?

....

b) Is a learner driver allowed to drive alone?

....

c) What car must you take for the test?

....

d) Why did the car in the test drive suddenly stop?

....

e) Where did the candidate make his test drive?

....

II. Choose between any, anyone, anything, anywhere – some, someone, something, somewhere – every, everyone – each:

a) Can .... in England take a driving test? –

b) – Yes, of course, but he must first have .... practice.

c) When I took my driving test, ... candidate got a test paper

with .... questions.

d) Did .... of the candidates have to pass a practical test? –

e) – Yes, of course. .... candidates came with their own car,

others had asked .... else to lend them theirs.

f) Did the examiner ask you .... else? –

g) – Yes, he did. He asked me .... about safety belts, but

I really don't remember .... question.

h) If you wanted to get .... information on driving tests, you

should be able to find a driving school ....
in the neighbourhood.

i) I only know there aren't .... schools around here.

MANZ Lernhilfen-Programm

H. Gumtau / W. Kurschatke

Englisch 5/6

Stoff des 1. Lernjahres

Wir üben in der 5. Jahrgangsstufe
Wir wiederholen in der 6. Jahrgangsstufe

Mit Lösungsheft

Neu bearbeitete Ausgabe

144 Seiten, illustriert,
DM 13,80

Bestell-Nr. 500

H. Gumtau / W. Kurschatke

Englisch 6/7

160 Seiten, illustriert, DM 13,80
Wir üben in der 6. bzw. 7. Jahrgangsstufe
Mit Lösungsheft
Bestell-Nr. 501

H. Gumtau / W. Kurschatke

English
Picture-guided
Comprehension

**10 leichte Comprehension-Tests mit
Bildern für das 2. und 3. Lernjahr und
zur Vorbereitung für die 7. Jahrgangsstufe der weiterführenden Schulen**

48 Seiten, DM 9,80

Dieses Arbeitsheft ist ein Trainings-
programm, mit dem sich jeder Schüler auf die
7. Jahrgangsstufe der Realschule oder einer
anderen weiterführenden Schule vorberei-
ten kann. Für den 7. Hauptschuljahrgang
dient dieses Buch als Wiederholung für den
Stoff der Jahrgangsstufen 5 und 6.

Bestell-Nr. 513

H. Gumtau / W. Kurschatke / G. Kirsch

Englisch –
Mittelstufe

8. bis 10. Jahrgangsstufe

Band 1:

Wir üben Wortschatz

Mit separatem Lösungsheft zu den Tests
159 Seiten, DM 14,80

Bestell-Nr. 296

Band 2:

Wir üben Grammatik

Verbesserte Ausgabe
Mit separatem Lösungsheft zu den Tests
159 Seiten, DM 14,80

Bestell-Nr. 297

Band 3:

Wir üben Rechtschreibung

Mit separatem Lösungsheft zu den Tests
159 Seiten, DM 14,80

Bestell-Nr. 298

Aufgaben, Lernhilfen, Lösungen, Tests

L. Haas / F. Höng

Rock- und Popsongs
im Englischunterricht

Sekundarstufe I und II

128 Seiten, DM 15,80

Eine umfangreiche Comprehension-
sammlung mit Popsongs, die ausführliche
Übungsteile zu folgenden Bereichen bietet:
Wortschatz – Grammatik – Fragen zum
Textverständnis – Weiterführende Fragen
und Diskussionspunkte – Sprechfertigkeit.
Mit Discographie.

Bestell-Nr. 543

MANZ Verlag · Anzinger Straße 1 · 8000 München 80